HEINEMANN MATHEMATICS 7
Teacher's Notes

For England and Wales . . .

Heinemann Mathematics and the National Curriculum

Heinemann Mathematics 7, 8 and 9 together are suitable for pupils working at levels 4, 5 and 6 of the National Curriculum.

	HM7	HM8	HM9
NC level	3 4 5 6 7		

For Scotland . . .

Heinemann Mathematics and Mathematics 5–14

Heinemann Mathematics, 7, 8 and 9 together are suitable for pupils working at levels D and E of the Mathematics 5–14 programme in Scotland.

	HM7	HM8	HM9
5–14 level	D E E+		

For Northern Ireland . . .

Heinemann Mathematics and the Common Curriculum

Heinemann Mathematics 7, 8 and 9 together are suitable for pupils working at levels 4, 5 and 6 of the Common Curriculum in Northern Ireland. A detailed match to the Common Curriculum is available as a separate document on request.

	HM7	HM8	HM9
CC level	4 5 6 7		

PREFACE

These notes are an integral and essential part of Heinemann Mathematics. As well as a general introduction to the course and a description of its structure, the notes provide the following detailed information for each section of work.

- Structure maps to show the links between Core, Support and Extension
- Mathematical Content and Development
- References to the National Curriculum and the Mathematics 5–14 Guidelines
- Equipment required
- Suggestions for Related, Introductory and Additional activities.
- Detailed comments and suggestions concerning particular questions.

AUTHORS
John T. Blair
James Carpy
Ian K. Clark
Aileen P. Duncan
Percy W. Farren
David W. A. McInnes
Dorothy S. Simpson

Heinemann Educational Publishers
Halley Court, Jordan Hill, Oxford OX2 8EJ
a division of Reed Educational & Professional Publishing Ltd

MELBOURNE AUCKLAND FLORENCE
PRAGUE MADRID ATHENS SINGAPORE
TOKYO SAO PAULO CHICAGO PORTSMOUTH (NH)
MEXICO IBADAN GABORONE JOHANNESBURG
KAMPALA NAIROBI

ISBN 0 435 03900 8

© Scottish Primary Mathematics Group 1992

First published 1992

Revised edition published 1995
99 98 97   10 9 8 7 6 5 4 3

Designed and produced by VAP Group, Kidlington, Oxon.

Printed and bound by Athenæum Press Ltd., Gateshead, Tyne & Wear.

CONTENTS

Teaching Notes

INTRODUCTION TO THE COURSE

The complete Heinemann Mathematics course aims to provide a programme of mathematics for pupils aged from 5 to 16.

The materials that comprise Heinemann Mathematics 7, 8 and 9 are suitable for pupils working at

- Levels 4, 5 and 6 of the National Curriculum (England and Wales)
- Levels D and E of the Mathematics 5 – 14 programme in Scotland
- Levels 4, 5 and 6 of the Common Curriculum (Northern Ireland).

Work is provided in relation to all the Attainment Targets in the above curricula at the Levels indicated with the exception of those Attainment Targets concerned with using computers.

The provision of Support material for less-able pupils and Extension material for more-able pupils is designed to ensure that, on completion of Heinemann Mathematics 9, Key Stage 3 pupils in England, Wales and Northern Ireland can demonstrate their ability to work at Level 5 or Level 6 or to some extent Level 7. The differentiated nature of the materials should also enable each pupil to embark on the appropriate level of GCSE or Standard Grade course at the appropriate time.

Some of the mathematical work in Heinemann Mathematics 7 was first published as part of *Mathematics: a development through activity* by Scottish Primary Mathematics Group. This has been extensively revised and restructured by a combined group of authors from SPMG and SSMG (Scottish Secondary Mathematics Group). Heinemann Mathematics 8 and 9 contain new material from SSMG whose aim has been to consolidate and build upon the most widely used mathematics programme in primary schools.

Rationale

Development

Pupils' understanding of mathematics should be progressive. As their course develops they should gain an overview of mathematics which is both wide and coherent and which goes well beyond the bare requirements set out in any list of attainment targets whether national or local. Clearly such progression is more readily obtained when care is taken to link new ideas directly with those previously encountered. The work for pupils throughout Heinemann Mathematics has been written with the need to ensure this progression to the fore. At the same time there is sufficient flexibility in the design of the materials to allow teachers and pupils to vary their route through the mathematics.

Continuity

Pupils' progress in mathematics should not be hindered by a lack of continuity, for example in resources or materials, in the use of mathematical language or in the teaching approaches adopted. Heinemann Mathematics addresses the needs of pupils throughout their schooling and thus contributes positively to a continuity of experience which in the past has often proved difficult to achieve, particularly when pupils move from primary to secondary school. Examples of *Teaching Approaches* applied throughout Heinemann Mathematics are given on page T2.

Activity

Pupils should experience mathematics in an active and practical way. The use of both structured and non-structured apparatus and the use of diagrams and pictures to help pupils acquire concepts and understand techniques is encouraged throughout Heinemann Mathematics. Practical work is advocated to secure concepts, develop meaningful language and to allow pupils to use and apply their mathematics.

Calculators

In our technologically-based society pupils are familiar, from an early age, with the use of calculators for computation. Calculators feature in Heinemann Mathematics with the intention that pupils should learn to use them intelligently. However, in different situations which necessitate computation, pupils should be able to use methods of calculation appropriate to these situations. Accordingly pupils are frequently expected to use paper-and-pencil methods as well as mental calculation.

Investigation

Pupils should be able to use their mathematics – facts, concepts, skills and thinking processes – to solve problems and to investigate. Throughout Heinemann Mathematics pupils are given opportunities to tackle problems – practical, real-life and mathematical – and it is recommended that topics are approached in an investigative way.

Contextualisation

Pupils should experience the use of mathematics in a wide variety of contexts including some which are cross-curricular in nature. Opportunities for demonstrating the important place of mathematics across the curriculum, in everyday life, in employment and in leisure – are virtually endless. An important feature of Heinemann Mathematics is the widespread presentation of mathematical ideas in contexts which are relevant to the pupils' world. Such contexts are more likely to stimulate their interest in mathematics and encourage positive attitudes.

Teaching Approaches

Pupils who have not in their earlier mathematical work made use of Heinemann Mathematics or the SPMG course but have been following a programme of study as described in any of the national curricula should be able to enter the Heinemann Mathematics course at any stage with confidence. There follows a description of teaching approaches used in earlier stages of Heinemann Mathematics or the SPMG course which are built upon in Heinemann Mathematics 7, 8 and 9 to give continuity of experience.

Problem Solving and Investigation

Many opportunities have been provided for the pupils to learn through practical activity, to apply mathematics to real-life problems and to explore and investigate mathematical ideas. They should have gradually developed an awareness of problem solving as a process in three broad steps, namely: getting started, doing the work, and reporting to others. The pupils' experiences of problem solving and investigation have been planned to

- allow them to use their mathematical knowledge and skills in new and unfamiliar situations
- develop their awareness of ideas of argument and proof
- develop their ability to communicate in mathematics.

Some of the work may be tackled at an individual level, particularly where it occurs among other examples on Core Textbook or Workbook pages. It is also beneficial on many occasions for problem solving to be carried out in pairs or in small groups of perhaps three or four pupils learning for themselves and from each other.

A systematic treatment of a range of stategies for problem solving is presented across Heinemann Mathematics 7, 8 and 9. These strategies are unlikely to be developed formally by the pupils for themselves and it is expected that they will require separate teaching.

Number

A consistent approach has been applied when developing written techniques for the four operations:

- concrete materials such as structured base ten apparatus are manipulated to arrive at a result
- when manipulating these materials emphasis is placed on establishing an appropriate language
- the manipulation of materials and the appropriate language are then linked to a written technique
- practice is provided to consolidate the written technique.

Subtraction

The method of subtraction which arises naturally from the manipulation of materials is *decomposition*. The following example illustrates a written technique which reflects the way the materials are manipulated and indicates the accompanying language.

$$
\begin{array}{rcl}
\text{T} & \text{U} & \cdot & \text{t} \\
{}^3\!\!\not{4} & {}^{14}\!\!\not{5} & \cdot & {}^{13} \\
- \; 1 & 6 & \cdot & 7 \\
\hline
2 & 8 & \cdot & 6
\end{array}
$$

7 tenths from 3 tenths. I cannot do this. Exchange 1 unit for 10 tenths to give 4 units and 13 tenths. 7 tenths from 13 tenths leaves 6 tenths.

6 units from 4 units. I cannot do this. Exchange 1 ten for 10 units to give 3 tens and 14 units. 6 units from 14 units leaves 8 units.

1 ten from 3 tens leaves 2 tens.

Division

The following example illustrates a written technique which reflects the process of *sharing* materials and indicates the accompanying language.

$$
\begin{array}{rcl}
& \text{T} & \text{U} & \cdot & \text{t} \\
& 2 & 5 & \cdot & 3 \\
3 \,\big| & 7 & {}^{1}6 & \cdot & {}^{1}5
\end{array}
$$

Share the 7 tens. 7 shared equally among 3 (or divided by 3) is 2, rem 1.

Share the 16 units. 16 shared equally among 3 is 5, rem 1.

Share the 15 tenths. 15 shared equally among 3 is 5.

When pupils encounter a word problem involving *grouping* language, as they frequently do, they must first establish that division is required and then use the technique illustrated above to find the result.

For division by a two-digit number pupils use a process of successive subtractions as follows. The accompanying language reflects the *context* of the problem, whether grouping or sharing is implied.

2549 cans of cola are to be packed in boxes each holding 12 cans. How many full boxes will there be? How many cans will be left over?

2549		← 2549 cans to be packed.
−1200	100	← 100 boxes use 1200 cans. (100 × 12 = 1200)
1349		← 1349 cans are left.
−1200	100	← 100 boxes use 1200 cans. (100 × 12 = 1200)
149		← 149 cans are left.
−120	10	← 10 boxes use 120 cans. (10 × 12 = 120)
29		← 29 cans are left.
−12	1	← 1 box uses 12 cans. (1 × 12 = 12)
17		← 17 cans are left.
−12	1	← 1 box uses 12 cans. (1 × 12 = 12)
5	212	

There will be 212 full boxes. 5 cans will be left over.

In general division by two (or more)-digit numbers is likely to be by calculator. Hence an emphasis is placed on its efficient use and on interpretation of the display.

Other methods

There are many situations in which the use of a standard written technique may not be the most appropriate method of computation. Pupils are expected to use alternative methods – written, mental and calculator – and to choose the most appropriate method for the computation in hand. Examples include:

- subtraction by 'counting on' when calculating change and when finding time differences
- mental multiplication and division by 10 and by 100
- mental estimation using single-digit rounding to check the reasonableness of a calculator result or a money total at a supermarket checkout.

Measure

The emphasis in the teaching approach to measure is very much on practical work. Nevertheless, written examples are also provided in each aspect of measure – length, weight, area, volume and time. Practical work is designed to secure concepts, give practice in measuring skills and develop language. Much of the content is presented within contexts so that learning is related to real-life situations.

The aspects of measure are developed along the following lines albeit at different rates:

- comparing and ordering experiences to develop relationships and associated language
- the use of arbitrary standards (for example, spans or cupfuls) to quantify measure and to show the need for an agreed standard measure
- the use of standard measures (for example, metres or litres) in estimating and measuring activities
- the use of fractional parts of these standard measures, leading to an awareness of the approximate nature of measure, that is, an awareness that any measurement is made to a selected degree of accuracy.

Although most measurements are carried out in metric standard units, Imperial units are also used where they are still in common use, for example, feet and inches for heights, miles for distances and gallons for volumes.

Shape and Position

The emphasis is again on practical work. From an early stage informal practical activities are used to develop the pupils' abilities to recognise shapes and their awareness of some properties of shapes. Pupils handle, examine, sort and build three-dimensional shapes. They cut out, fit, move, fold, sort and examine two-dimensional shapes. Plasticine, card, paper, nailboards and Meccano-type strips are used to make shapes. As the pupils' measuring skills develop and they explore real-life situations, work in Shape and Measure are integrated, for example, formulae for the area of a triangle and the volume of a cuboid are applied.

The aesthetic and recreational appeal of working with patterns of coloured shapes, tessellations, shape puzzles, curve stitching, symmetrical shapes and so on is powerful and can have positive effects on the pupils' view of mathematics in general. Pupils who experience difficulty for example, in Number work, can often gain confidence through their achievements in Shape work.

Handling data

The pupils' experiences of handling data and information are already wide and have been developed progressively. In providing work to develop the relevant concepts and skills emphasis is placed on

- collecting data: this involves pupils in identifying data they wish to collect as well as designing observation sheets and carrying out practical surveys
- organising data: this develops from simple sorting activities to the use of 'tick' sheets and later more sophisticated frequency tables requiring pupils to choose suitable class intervals
- displaying data: methods of display progress from the use of real objects and the use of pictures to the construction of a wide range of graphs; pupils are made aware of relative strengths and weaknesses of different forms of graphs and are asked to select the most appropriate form for given data and their own data
- interpreting data: this involves pupils in answering questions about a given graph as well as devising questions about graphs they themselves have constructed.

In addition, other resources such as computer databases and graph-plotting packages should continue to be used to expand and develop the pupils' experience of handling data.

STRUCTURE OF THE COURSE

Format

Material is provided at three levels:

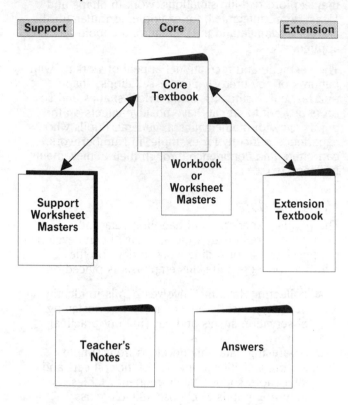

Core Textbook and Workbook

The Core material comprises a Textbook and an associated Workbook (which is also available as photocopiable Worksheet Masters). The Textbook is divided into four parts which should be tackled in the order in which they appear. Each *Part* contains a number of sections covering different aspects of mathematics. Within each *Part* the order in which sections are tackled is not important, allowing flexibility in planning programmes of study. The top of each Textbook page contains the following information:

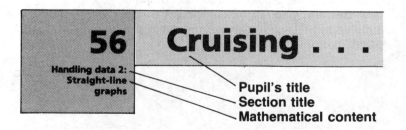

Workbook pages are used in conjunction with the Core Textbook. This expendable material is designed to avoid pupils spending unnecessary amounts of time copying tables, diagrams and graphs. It also provides templates for cut-out shapes and, on occasions, a structured layout to help develop recording skills.

The following symbols and instructions appear on the pages:

 indicates the use of associated Workbook material

Go back to Textbook . . . refers pupils back to the appropriate Core Textbook reference

Ask your teacher what to do next. indicates the end of a section.

Support

This material is provided in the form of photocopiable Worksheet Masters, although on occasions pupils are directed to answer some questions in their jotters (copy books, exercise books). Not every section of the Core Textbook has associated Support work. Where experience suggests that some pupils may have difficulty progressing far in the Core material, Support work is provided in one of two forms.

- Lead-in work is at a simpler level to that of the Core, designed to provide preparatory work related to the Core.
- Parallel work contains similar content to that of the Core but is set at a simpler level, in less demanding contexts and develops ideas more slowly.

 indicates that the questions should be answered in jotters.

Extension

In the Extension Textbook material is provided related to certain sections. In general, in Heinemann Mathematics 7 and 8 little new work is introduced, rather the contexts in which the work is set become more demanding. However, in Heinemann Mathematics 9, much of the Extension introduces new content to provide able pupils with the necessary grounding for the most demanding levels of the Standard Grade and GCSE courses. Answers are supplied in the back of the Extension Textbook.

Answer Book

Answers to Support and Core work only are supplied in a single book.

Teacher's Notes

Throughout this book the following abbreviations are used to refer to other pupil component pages:

- (just page number) – Core Textbook
- W (+ page number) – Workbook
- S (+ page number) – Support
- E (+ page number) – Extension

Class Organisation

The material has been designed and written to cope with the demands of teaching to mixed ability or set classes. It is flexible in its application and can be used to support a variety of different forms of class organisation:

- whole class
- groups, ability or social
- individuals.

All these forms of class organisation have their place, and indeed there are real benefits to be gained from varying the organisation to suit different situations.

Whatever form of class organisation is used, the material gives teachers the opportunity to teach, and indeed the need for a positive, regular input from teachers is paramount.

More detailed advice on class organisation is given in the section *Using the Course in the Classroom* and in the detailed page-by-page notes for each section.

Using the Course in the Classroom

Preparation

It is important that the teacher takes the time to read the Teacher's Notes for each section of work before teaching that section. These notes provide valuable information in the form of a Section Overview and a set of Page-by-Page Notes.

Section Overview

- Structure map showing the relationship among Core, Support and Extension
- Content and Development detailing assumed knowledge and the work of the section
- National Curricula references showing how the work contributes to the pupils' experience of the individual Attainment Targets
- Equipment list indicating the requirements for the section
- Related activities to complement the work of the section.

Page-by-Page Notes

- National Curricula references showing how the work of the page contributes to the pupils' experience of the individual Attainment Targets
- Content detailing the mathematical ideas contained on the page
- Equipment list indicating the requirements for the page
- Organisation where a particular teaching approach is required or recommended
- Introductory activities suggesting possible teaching approaches
- Detailed advice referring to specific questions
- Additional activities suggesting possible follow-up work.

Beginning a Section of Work

It is anticipated that most if not all the pupils in a class will begin a section of work at the same time, giving the opportunity for introductory teaching, scene-setting activities and discussion, possibly making use of the suggested introductory activities. As the work develops it is likely that pupils will progress at different rates, giving rise to the formation of a small number of groups.

It may be appropriate for some pupils to be directed to Support material early in the section and for some of the more able pupils to be given Extension work at the end of the section. In this way teaching and discussion can be directed effectively either to the whole class, to a group of pupils or to individuals as appropriate. The class should come together again to begin the next section of work.

Routes Through a Section

A description of the relationship among Core, Support and Extension pages and a diagram showing this relationship and possible routes through each section are given in the Teacher's Notes for each section. The most likely route is indicated in the structure map by continuous lines. Alternative routes are indicated by dotted lines. An example is given below.

Although most pupils may be capable of making a start in the Core Textbook, the teacher may wish certain pupils to begin with the Support materials. It is neither necessary nor desirable for every pupil to do all the work on every page. A balanced selection of work should be made according to the pupils' abilities.

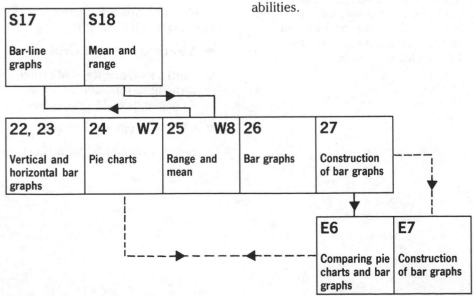

Teaching

The materials must not be regarded as a programmed text. Preliminary teaching is generally necessary before the pupils attempt the Textbook and Workbook pages. Moreover, although the Textbook and Workbook pages do include brief instructions and explanations, it is essential that the teacher reads and discusses these with the pupils to ensure that they are fully understood before the pupils proceed with the work.

Special Features

Symbols

 This symbol appears alongside some questions, often at the end of certain pages, and indicates that these questions are of a more demanding nature.

 Certain sections and whole pages are devoted to investigative work. This symbol has been used to identify questions which provide additional opportunities for pupils to develop and use problem solving skills.

 This symbol indicates a reminder of key information essential for the work of the page.

Detours

A **Detour** is designed to widen the mathematical experience of the pupils. **Detours** are presented as single pages of work distributed throughout Heinemann Mathematics 7, 8 and 9. They provide work which is important and worthwhile but which is not necessarily related to the work of a specific area of content. The work in the **Detours** often requires an exploratory, investigative approach which draws upon the pupils' problem solving skills. In many cases the topics lend themselves to further development.

Detours are provided at Support, Core and Extension levels and form a pool of self-contained activities which can be dipped into from time to time. They can be used in different ways, for example

- by individuals or groups who have completed their set work early
- by a group or whole class to provide a change of focus in their work
- to provide, on occasions, additional problem solving activities and challenges.

The **Detours** should *not* be attempted as though they form a single section of work. However, for convenience, The Teacher's Notes for the **Detours** within each part have been grouped together and placed at the end of the Notes for that *Part*.

Extended Contexts

Contexts are used throughout Heinemann Mathematics to present and develop mathematical ideas. A context may feature on a single Textbook or Workbook page; sometimes the theme is continued on two or more pages. An **Extended context**, however, deals with the same theme over a whole section of the course.

There are two extended contexts at each stage containing simulated activities which form the basis for developing mathematical work which is real in its usefulness and application. Most of the mathematical concepts and skills involved are familiar to the pupils although some may only have been recently developed.

In organising and managing the work of the **Extended context** the teacher should consider the following principles:

- The **Extended context** need not be tackled as a continuous piece of work. Some teachers may choose to enhance the on-going mathematics programme by dipping into the **Extended context** from time to time.
- The contexts include many activities which can be attempted by *all* pupils. However, since there is work for pupils of different levels of ability it is advised that pupils should, on many occasions, work in groups. These can be formed on the basis of similar ability, mixed ability or social considerations.
- It is almost certain that no pupils will attempt every activity. It is likely that some groups will omit a part or parts of a context. Also, different groups may work simultaneously on separate aspects of a context.

It is important, therefore, that at appropriate times, when group activity has been completed, a full class discussion of the work done takes place. Pupils should report orally to others; they should be asked to write about their work, to explain results, and to interpret diagrams and graphs which have been produced. Wall displays should be mounted. Part of the teacher's role is to maximise the involvement of *all* the pupils in the work of the context, either directly in carrying out the suggested activities, or indirectly through discussion of the work of others.

Progress Records

A number of items are offered to help teachers record the progress of their pupils.

- A **Record of Work Grid**
- **Pupil Progress Records** linked to the National Curriculum (England and Wales) and the Mathematics 5–14 Guidelines (Scotland).
- A **Class Progress Record**.

A full description can be found on page T12.

References to Attainment Targets

Detailed references to attainment targets for the National Curriculum (England and Wales) and the Mathematics 5–14 Guidelines (Scotland) are included in these Teacher's Notes in both the Section Overview and the Page-by-Page Notes. These references are provided as an aid to planning and recording. There is no intention to suggest that teaching should follow the targets in a slavish way.

A summary of the coverage of Heinemann Mathematics 7 is given for the National Curriculum (England and Wales) on page T29 and for the Mathematics 5–14 Guidelines on page T30. In each summary chart, a blank space indicates coverage of work towards a particular attainment target or strand.

England and Wales

■ The Teacher's Notes contain detailed references to the Programme of Study statements within the five Sections at Key Stage 3. The following code is used to identify the Sections:

Using and Applying Mathematics	UA	Shape, Space and Measure	SM
Number	N	Handling Data	HD
Algebra	A		

The referencing shows each Section, Subsection, Part and NC Level. For example:

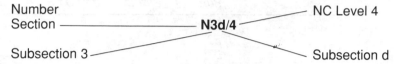

(Understanding when and how to use fractions and percentages to make proportional comparisons)

■ Some of the outcomes specified in the Programme of Study statements relate to skills or concepts which children develop over an extended period. In these circumstances the NC Level is sometimes indicated by an arrow. For example:

$$N3d/4 \rightarrow 5$$

refers to Number work appropriate to children at Level 4 'working towards' a statement which is at Level 5 in the Level Descriptions.

■ The work in a section or single page of Heinemann Mathematics 7 frequently relates to more than one Section or Subsection of the Programme of Study. On these occasions, for economy of presentation, statements at the same Level in a Section are combined. For example:

$$N3de, 4a/5$$

■ Within each Attainment Target, Programme of Study Section 1 overarches all the other Sections. As the Heinemann Mathematics course includes coverage of all the statements in these other Sections, separate references to Section 1 statements are not made.

Scotland

In the Mathematics 5–14 Guidelines, the strands within each attainment outcome are not numbered or lettered. We have therefore devised a system of referencing using a code based on the initial letter(s) of each strand and the appropriate level. The coding is as follows:

Number, Money and Measurement	Code	Shape, Position and Movement	Code
Range and Type of Numbers	**RTN**	Range of Shapes	**RS**
Money	**M**	Position and Movement	**PM**
Add and Subtract	**AS**	Symmetry	**S**
Multiply and Divide	**MD**	Angle	**A**
Round Numbers	**RN**		
Fractions, Percentages and Ratio	**FPR**	**Problem-Solving and Enquiry**	**PSE**
Patterns and Sequences	**PS**	**Information Handling**	
Functions and Equations	**FE**	Collect	**C**
Measure and Estimate	**ME**	Organise	**O**
Time	**T**	Display	**D**
Perimeter, Formulae, Scales	**PFS**	Interpret	**I**

The referencing shows strand code, level and attainment target. For example:

MD/E2 — Second target
(Multiply and divide mentally for any numbers including decimals by 10, 100, 1000 in applications in number, measurement and money.)

Multiply and Divide
Level E

On occasion the referencing indicates only the strand code and level. This occurs when the attainment targets do not provide an adequate description of the work.

Work beyond Level E is indicated using E+.
Where E+ appears alongside other references then an element of the work is at that level.
Where E+ appears on its own then all of the work is at that level.

Northern Ireland

References to the Common Curriculum (Northern Ireland) are coded as in the published curriculum.

HEINEMANN MATHEMATICS 7

Equipment

Basic equipment

The following is assumed to be available.

Paper: A4 plain; 2 mm, $\frac{1}{2}$ cm, 1 cm squared; 1 cm isometric; 1 cm isometric dot; card; tracing

Other: 1 centimetre cubes, 360° protractors, calculators, coloured pencils, counters, dice, elastic bands, glue, long metric tapes, marker pen, metre sticks, metric tapes, pairs of compasses, paper clips, pipe cleaners, rulers, scissors, set squares, sticky tape, straws, string or thread

Additional equipment

Equipment	Part 1	Part 2	Part 3	Part 4
white paper plates	13			
mirrors	E2			
newspapers – football scores	27			
dried beans (1 kg)	28			E36–37
weighing scales	28		E22	
dominoes	E8			
paper – 2 cm squared	28			118
calendars for several years including leap years	S13			
paper – large sheets		38		104–105
atlas		W14		
coins – 2p, at least forty		S26		
shapes for tiling/pattern		49	88	
material for a plumb line and a spirit level		50		
thermometer for outside temperature		55		
profits table (enlarged version)			E17	
plastic cup, 2 litre bottle			E21	
parcel/tin filled with sand			E22	
worksheets of blank numberlines			60, 76	
copy of the *Highway Code*			62	
cups, mugs, tins, jars, etc.			68–69, E23	
measuring jars including 1 litre jar			68–69, E23	
stones and other objects which sink			E23	
prepared cards			75	
calendars – current			81	110–111
postmarks from envelopes/postcards			81	
timelines			82–83, S37–40	
playing cards			85–86	
coins – 1p, 2p and 5p			85–86	
opaque polythene bags			86	
newspapers – double-page sheets only			88	
pegs and peg boards			88	
marbles, card – six 36 cm strips			90	
notepaper and envelopes			90	
ball			90	
sand or salt or sugar (500 cm³)			90	
timer for seconds				98–100
tiles or gummed shapes of regular polygons				104
poles or canes about 1·5 m				E34–35
paper circles (large)				E34–35
newspapers – times of sunrise and sunset				E34–35
paper – 5 cm squared				118
paper – 1 cm squared (40 cm × 40 cm)				110–111

(just a number) – Core Textbook
S – Support Worksheet Masters

W – Core Workbook or Worksheet Masters
E – Extension Textbook

Extra equipment required for the Introductory and Additional activities

Equipment	
Part 1	
newspaper and computer software for newspaper layout	*1*
dominoes and prepared card dominoes	*S3*
measuring equipment with scales marked in tenths	*S8*
cardboard scales or scales drawn on OHP slide	*19*
sketches of objects, for example, trees, ships, etc.	*20*
model car	*S15*
pie charts from newspapers/magazines	*E6*
clothes catalogue or magazine	*29*
crossword solutions from newspapers/magazines	*S6*
Part 2	
parcels with weights marked	*33*
catalogue, shopping items	*34–35*
prepared diagram	*36*
OHP slide with square grid	*W11*
pair of card congruent right-angled triangles	*37*
card rectangle	*S24*
paper circles and/or squares	*39*
multipack labels showing number and cost/weight, etc.	*48, S28–29*
jointed rods	*49*
set of prepared cardboard angles	*49*
travel company brochure containing weather information	*S30*
Part 3	
measuring instruments for weight and volume	*73*
packages and containers showing volumes/weights	*73*
sets of prepared cards	*74–75*
magnetic compass and large cardboard 360° protractor	*78–79*
sequence of daily newspapers	*81*
weekly and monthly magazines	*81*
local air, bus, train timetables	*83*
concert/theatre timetables	*S37*
prepared letter cards	*85–87*
labels showing weights in kilograms and pounds	*84*
maps showing kilometres/miles conversion information	*84*
prepared card shapes	*S35*
prepared sheet of regular pentagons and hexagons	*S35*
Part 4	
ream of paper	*98*
playing cards	*98–99*
novel	*98–99*
pack of prepared cards	*95*

(just a number) – Core Textbook   *W – Core Workbook or Worksheet Masters*
S – Support Worksheet Masters   *E – Extension Textbook*

MATHEMATICAL DEVELOPMENT OF HEINEMANN MATHEMATICS 7 Mathematics in the National Curriculum (England and Wales)

Part	Using and applying mathematics	Number: Knowledge and use of numbers	Number: Measures	Algebra	Shape and space	Handling data
1	Strategies – guess and check – listing Detour – number investigation (S)	Whole numbers – numbers in the environment – large numbers, approximation – addition and subtraction – multiplication by 2 to 10, 100 and a two-digit whole number – division by 2 to 10 – calculator work – other methods of calculation Detours – multiples and factors – checking calculations (E) Decimals – 1st and 2nd decimal place – addition and subtraction (money) – multiplication by 2 to 10, 100 and a two-digit whole number – division by 2 to 10 – multiplication using a calculator – division by 2 to 10	Length – introducing the millimetre Scale – scale drawings – drawing to scale – construction of a 3D model (E) Detour – calendar (S)		Circle designs Line symmetry (E) Enlarging symmetrical patterns (E) Detours – shape puzzle (S) – position fixing (S)	Bar graphs Pie charts Range and mean Frequency tables Comparison of pie charts with bar graphs (E)
	Extended Context: The Goodies Catalogue					
2	Detour – investigation	Whole numbers – division by 2 to 10 and by a two-digit whole number – proportion Detour – sets of numbers (S) Decimals – length, money and weight calculations – division by 2 to 10 – approximate costs Fractions – one quantity as a fraction of another – equivalence – addition and subtraction of halves and quarters	Area – rectangle $A = l \times b$ – right-angled triangles – square kilometre – composite shapes (E)	Detours – equalities and inequalities – word formulae	3D Shape – prisms, pyramids and composite shapes – regular solids – planes of symmetry (E) Angles – types of angles – horizontal, vertical, perpendicular and parallel lines	Trend graphs Straight-line graphs Curved-line graphs (E) Travel graphs (E)
	Extended Context: The School Concert (E)					
3	Strategies – patterns – practical activities – mixed strategies – elimination (E)	Whole numbers – division of large numbers using a calculator Decimals – approximation to nearest whole number – interpretation of answers – calculation of exact remainder – 3rd decimal place – approximation to 1st decimal place Fractions – whole number times fraction/mixed number – fraction of a whole number	Volume – reading scales – cuboid $V = l \times b \times h$ – immersion (E) Time – calendar work – 12- and 24-hour times – durations Detours – metric/imperial relationships – distance tables (E)		Symmetry – rotational symmetry Angles – calculations – bearings – measuring and drawing Detours – shapes within shapes (S) – overlap shapes (S)	Probability – language – outcomes – the probability scale
	Extended Context: The Field Study Week Contexts: Glenafton Weather Station (E), Abermore Trout Farm (E)					
4	Detour – digit sum investigation (E)	Whole numbers – multiplication and division by multiples of 10 and 100 Detour – inverse operations Decimals – multiplication and division of money by multiples of 10 and 100 Percentages – concept, calculations – calculations based on 10% – link with fractions and decimals – percentage increase and decrease (E)	Rate and Speed – rate per minute/second/hour	Negative numbers – language and notation – ordering – informal addition and subtraction	Tessellations – geometric shapes – patterns Detour – matching shapes (S)	Designing observation sheets Class intervals

S – Support Worksheet masters   E – Extension Textbook

MATHEMATICAL DEVELOPMENT OF HEINEMANN MATHEMATICS 7

Mathematics 5–14 (Scotland)

Part	Problem-Solving and Enquiry	Information Handling	Number, Money and Measurement — Whole numbers	Fractions, decimals and percentages	Algebra and relationships	Measure	Shape, Position and Movement
1	Strategies – guess and check – listing Detour – number investigation (S)	Bar graphs Pie charts Range and mean Frequency tables Comparison of pie charts with bar graphs (E)	Numbers in the environment Large numbers, approximation Addition and subtraction Multiplication by 2 to 10, 100 and by a two-digit whole number Division by 2 to 10 Calculator work Other methods of calculation Detours – multiples and factors – checking calculations (E)	Decimals – 1st and 2nd decimal place – addition and subtraction (money) – multiplication by 2 to 10 and 100 and a two-digit whole number – multiplication using a calculator – division by 2 to 10		Length – introducing the millimetre Scale – scale drawings – drawing to scale – construction of a 3D model (E) Detour – calendar (S)	Circle designs Line symmetry (E) Enlarging symmetrical patterns (E) Detours – shape puzzle (S) – position fixing (S)
	Extended Context: The Goodies Catalogue						
2	Detour – investigation	Trend graphs Straight-line graphs Curved-line graphs (E) Travel graphs (E)	Division by 2 to 10 and by a two-digit whole number Proportion Detour – sets of numbers (S)	Decimals – length, money and weight calculations – division by 2 to 10 – approximation costs Fractions – one quantity as a fraction of another – equivalence – addition and subtraction of halves and quarters	Detours – equalities and inequalities – word formulae	Area – rectangle $A = l \times b$ – right-angled triangles – square kilometre – composite shapes (E)	3D shape – prisms, pyramids and composite shapes – regular solids – planes of symmetry (E) Angles – types of angles – horizontal, vertical, perpendicular and parallel lines
	Extended Context: The School Concert (E)						
3	Strategies – patterns – practical activities – mixed strategies – elimination (E)	Probability – language – outcomes – the probability scale	Division of large numbers using a calculator	Decimals – approximation to nearest whole number – interpretation of answers – calculation of exact remainder – 3rd decimal place – approximation to 1st decimal place Fractions – whole number times fraction/mixed number – fraction of a whole number		Volume – reading scales – cuboid $V = l \times b \times h$ – immersion (E) Time – calendar work – 12- and 24- hour times – durations Detours – metric/imperial relationships – distance tables (E)	Symmetry – rotational symmetry Angles – calculations – bearings – measuring and drawing Detours – shapes within shapes (S) – overlap shapes (S)
	Extended Context: The Field Study Week Contexts: Glenafton Weather Station (E), Abermore Trout Farm (E)						
4	Detour – digit sum investigation (E)	Designing observation sheets Class intervals	Multiplication and division by multiples of 10 and 100 Detour – inverse operations	Decimals – multiplication and division of money by multiples of 10 and 100 Percentages – concept, calculations – calculations based on 10% – link with fractions and decimals – percentage increase and decrease (E)	Negative numbers – language and notation – ordering – informal addition and subtraction	Rate and speed – rate per minute/ second/hour	Tessellations – geometric shapes – patterns Detour – matching shapes (S)
	Extended Context: The Field Study Week						

S – Support Worksheet Masters   E – Extension Textbook

Progress Records

A number of items are offered to help teachers record the progress of their pupils.

At the end of the Core Workbook:
- A **Record of Work Grid**

In these Teacher's Notes:
- **Pupil Progress Records** linked to the National Curriculum (England and Wales) (pages T13–T16) and the Mathematics 5–14 Guidelines (Scotland) (pages T17–T20).
- A **Class Progress Record** (pages T21–T24).

Teachers can choose to what extent they use these materials.

Record of Work Grid

The grid at the end of the Core Workbook or photocopiable Worksheet Masters consists of a set of numbered boxes which correspond exactly to every page of the Core Textbook, Core Workbook, Support Worksheets and Extension Textbook. The grid provides a simple, convenient way of recording work attempted or completed by individual pupils. At its simplest, pupils could be instructed to tick boxes as they complete the work. However, teachers may wish to adopt a more sophisticated system, using colour codes, a variety of ticks or other symbols to indicate, for example, 'completion' or 'partial completion'.

Pupil Progress Records

A choice of Pupil Progress Records is provided showing links to the National Curriculum (England and Wales) (pages T13–T16) and the Mathematics 5–14 Guidelines (Scotland) (pages T17–T20). For each curriculum, four sheets are provided corresponding to Heinemann Mathematics 7 *Parts 1–4*.

The pupil's progress in each section can be summarised in the right-hand column using a code such as:

- ☐ – not attempted
- ◨ – some difficulty
- ◧ – satisfactory
- ■ – excellent

There is additional space for an overall summary of the year's work which could include general comments on progress, attitude, effort, special difficulties and so on.

It is expected that this record of progress will be maintained by the teacher and will show achievement rather than be a simple list of work attempted. Achievement will be measured in a variety of ways which are likely to include appropriate assessment items as well as teacher observation of on-going class work.

Class Progress Records

This provides an alternative method of recording the progress of a number of pupils.

Pupil progress record: *Part 1*

HEINEMANN MATHEMATICS 7

Name: _____

Class: _____

England and Wales
National Curriculum
Statements of Attainment

National Curriculum Statements of Attainment	S	C	E

Whole numbers 1
Numbers in the environment; approximation; addition and subtraction; multiplication; division by 2 to 10

	S	C	E
N3ab/3; 2a, 3ab/4, 3f/4 → 5	☐		
UA3d/3; 3ad/4 → 5; 2a/5 N2a, 3e/3; 2a, 3ab, 4a/4 HD2a/4		☐	

Other methods 1
Single digit calculations; associative law

	S	C	E
UA4a/5 N3b/4; 3f/4 → 5		☐	

Shape patterns
Circle designs

Line symmetry; enlarging symmetrical patterns

	S	C	E
SM 2ab/4 → 5		☐	
UA 3ce/4; 2c/5 → 6 SM2ab/4 → 5; 2bc, 3b/5			☐

Decimals 1
1st and 2nd decimal place; addition and subtraction; multiplication by 2 to 10, 100, and by calculator

	S	C	E
N2ab, 3ce/3; 2a, 3c/3 → 4; 2ab, 3c, 4b/4; 3c, 4ab/4 → 5 SM4b/3 → 4		☐	
N3e/4; 2ab/4 → 5; 3ce/5 SM4a/5			☐

Length and scale
Introducing the millimetre; scale drawing; drawing to scale

	S	C	E
SM4b/4; 4a/5; 3d/5 → 6	☐		
UA2bd, 3c/5 SM4b/4; 4a/5; 3d/5 → 6; 3d/6		☐	
SM2b/4; 3d/5 → 6			☐

Handling data 1
Bar graphs; mean; range; tallying and frequency tables; pie charts; bar-line graphs

	S	C	E
HD2cf/4; 2d/5	☐		
N3d/4 HD2abc/4; 2c/4 → 6; 2def/5		☐	
HD2a/4; 2fg/5; 2f/5 → 6			☐

Problem solving 1
Guess and check; listing

	S	C	E
UA2ac/4	☐		
UA2ac/4		☐	
UA2a/4			☐

Detours
Shape puzzle

	S	C	E
UA2ac/5	☐		

Position fixing

	S	C	E
UA3d/5 SM3a/4	☐		

Calendar

	S	C	E
UA3ad/4; 2/c5	☐		

Investigation

	S	C	E
UA4b/4 A2b/4	☐		

Multiples and factors

	S	C	E
UA3c/4 N2a, 3a/4			☐

Checking calculations

	S	C	E
UA4b/5 N3a, 4c/5			☐

HEINEMANN MATHEMATICS 7

Pupil progress record: *Part 2*

Name: _____

Class: _____

	England and Wales National Curriculum Statements of Attainment	S	C	E
Decimals 2 Length; money; weight	UA3b/5 N3c, 4ab/4 SM4a/4; 4ab/5 HD2a/4		☐	
Other methods 2 Approximate costs	N3c/4; 3f/5		☐	
Area Rectangles; right-angled triangles; large units; composite shapes	SM4d/4; 4d/4 → 6; 4d/5 → 6	☐		
	SM4d/4 → 6; 4a/5; 4d/5 → 6; 4d/6		☐	
	SM4d/5 → 6; 4d/6			☐
Fractions 1 Equivalence; addition and subtraction of halves and quarters	N2b/4; 3c/5 → 6		☐	
3D Shape Prisms and pyramids from nets; regular shapes	SM2ab/4	☐		
	SM2ab/4; 2ab/5		☐	
Planes of symmetry	SM2ab/4 → 5; 2c/5			☐
Division 1 Division of whole numbers and 1st and 2nd place decimals by 2 to 10; proportion	N3b/4; 3c/5; 4a/5 → 6	☐		
	N3b/4; 3c/5; 4a/5 → 6		☐	
	N3e, 4a/5 → 6			☐
Angles 1 Types of angles; horizontal, vertical, parallel and perpendicular lines	UA2b, 3ac/4; 2abc/5 SM2d/4 → 5; 2d/5		☐	
Whole numbers 2 Multiplication and division by 2 digits (pencil and paper methods)	N3b/5			☐
Handling data 2 Trend and straight-line graphs	A3c/5 SM4d/4 HD2cf/5	☐		
	A2c/5 HD2acf/4; 2cf/5			☐
Travel and curved-line graphs	A2c/5; 2c/6 → 7 HD2cf/5; 2cf/6			☐
Detours Sets of numbers	UA3d/3 N3a/3 → 4 HD2c/3	☐		
Equalities and inequalities	UA3ab/5 N2a/4			☐
Word formulae	A3b/5			☐
Investigation	UA4bd/5			☐

Pupil progress record: *Part 3*

Name: _____

Class: _____

	England and Wales National Curriculum Statements of Attainment	S	C	E
Extended context The School Concert	UA1ab/4; 2abc, 3cd/5; 2c/6 N3c/5; 4ab/5 → 6; 4ab/6 SM3d/6			☐
Division 2 Using a calculator; interpretation of answers	N3e, 4b/5		☐	
	N3bce, 4b/5; 4d/5 → 6 HD2ad/5 → 6		☐	
Symmetry Rotational symmetry	SM2c, 3b/5		☐	
Fractions 2 Whole number times fraction/mixed number; fraction of a whole number	N3ce, 4ab/5		☐	
Volume Reading scales; volume of a cuboid	SM4abd/4; 4d/5 → 6		☐	
Immersion	SM4b/4; 4d/5 → 6			☐
Decimals 3 Third decimal place; place value; rounding to 1st decimal place	N2a/5; 4d/5 → 6 SM4b/4; 4a/5		☐	
Angles 2 Calculations; bearings; measuring and drawing angles	SM2d/5; 2d, 3a/5 → 6		☐	
	SM2d/5; 3a/5 → 6; 2d/6			☐
Time Calendar; 12 and 24 hour times; durations	N4b/4 SM4a/3 → 4; 4a/4	☐		
	UA4a/4 N4ab/4 SM4ab/4		☐	
	UA2ad/4; 2c, 3b/5 N4b/4 SM4a/4			☐
Probability Language; outcomes; scale	HD3a/4; 3abd/4 → 5	☐		
	HD3ae/4; 3abd/5		☐	
Problem solving 2 Patterns; practical investigations Mixed strategies; elimination	A2b/4	☐		
	UA2abc/5 A2b/4		☐	
	UA2abc, 4d/5 A2b/4 SM3d/5 → 6			☐
Detours Shapes within shapes	SM2ab/4		☐	
Overlap shapes	SM2ab/4		☐	
Metric/Imperial relationships	SM4a/5			☐
Distance tables	UA3bd/5			☐

Pupil progress record: *Part 4*

Name: _____

Class: _____

England and Wales
National Curriculum
Statements of Attainment

Topic	Statements	S	C	E
Percentages Concept; using common percentages; link with fractions and decimals	N2b/4; 3c/4 → 5; 3d/5 → 6 HD2c/5 → 6		☐	
	N2b/4; 3c/4 → 5; 3c/5; 2b/5 → 6; 3d/6 HD2c/5 → 6			☐
	N3c, 4b/5 → 6; 3d/6			☐
Other methods 3 Multiplication and division by multiples of 10 and 100	N3bc, 4b/5		☐	
Rate and speed Rate per minute/second/hour	N4a/5; 4d/5 → 6 SM4c/5 → 7; 4c/6 → 7			☐
Negative numbers Concept; language; increase and decrease	N2b/3; 2b, 3c/4 → 5			☐
Tessellations Geometric shapes; patterns	UA3ce/4 SM2ab, 3bc/4; 2b, 3bc/5			☐
Handling data 3 Designing observation sheets; class intervals	UA3e/4 HD2ac/4; 2ce/5; 2cf/6			☐
Extended context The Field Study Week	UA2c, 3b/4; 2c/5; 2acd, 4e/6 N2b, 3cd, 4b/5 A3b/5 SM2bc, 3a/4; 2d, 3d/5; 3d/5 → 6; 3d/6; 4a/7			☐
Contexts Glenafton Weather Station	UA3bcd/6 N4b/5 HD2cf/6			☐
Abermore Trout Farm	N3c/5; 4a/6 SM4c/7 HD2f/5			☐
Detours Matching shapes	SM2ab/2	☐		
Inverse operations	N4c/5		☐	
Digit sum investigation	UA2bc, 4b/6 N3a/4			☐

Summary

HEINEMANN MATHEMATICS 7

Name: _____

Class: _____

	Scotland Mathematics 5–14 Attainment targets	S	C	E

Whole numbers 1
Numbers in the environment; approximation;
addition and subtraction; multiplication; division
by 2 to 10

	S	C	E
RTN/C; AS/C, D; MD/C, D; RN/C, D		☐	
PSE; RTN/D; AS/E; MD/C, D; RN/D, E			☐

Other methods 1
Single digit calculations; associative law

	S	C	E
PSE; AS/C, D, E; MD/D; RN/D, E			☐

Shape patterns
Circle designs

	S	C	E
RS/C, D; S/D			☐

Line symmetry; enlarging symmetrical patterns

	S	C	E
RS/C, D; S/D; E+			☐

Decimals 1
1st and 2nd decimal place; addition and
subtraction; multiplication by 2 to 10, 100, and
by calculator

	S	C	E
PSE; RTN/D; AS/D; MD/D	☐		
PSE; RTN/D; AS/D; MD/D; ME/D; PFS/E			☐

Length and scale
Introducing the millimetre; scale drawing;
drawing to scale

	S	C	E
RTN/D; ME/D, E; PFS/E	☐		
PSE; RTN/D; RN/D; ME/D, E; PFS/E			☐
RTN/D; ME/D, E; PFS/E; RS/D, E			☐

Handling data 1
Bar graphs; mean; range; tallying and frequency
tables; pie charts; bar-line graphs

	S	C	E
O/C; D/C; I/C; MD/D	☐		
C/C, D, E; O/C, D; D/C, D; I/C, D, E			☐
PSE; D/C, D; I/D, E			☐

Problem solving 1
Guess and check; listing

	S	C	E
PSE	☐		
PSE		☐	
PSE			☐

Detours

	S	C	E
Shape puzzle — PSE; S/D	☐		
Position fixing — PM/D	☐		
Calendar — PSE; I/C	☐		
Investigation — MD/C	☐		
Multiples and factors — MD/D; PS/C			☐
Checking calculations — PSE			☐

© Heinemann Educational 1992

Pupil progress record: *Part 2*

Name: _____

Class: _____

	Scotland Mathematics 5–14 Attainment targets	S	C	E
---	---	:-::	:-:	:-:
Decimals 2 Length; money; weight	PSE; RTN/D; AS/D; MD/D; ME/C, D		☐	
Other methods 2 Approximate costs	RTN/C; AS/D; RN/D		☐	
Area Rectangles; right-angled triangles; large units; composite shapes	ME/C, D; PFS/E	☐		
	ME/C, D, E; PFS/E		☐	
Fractions 1 Equivalence; addition and subtraction of halves and quarters	RTN/E		☐	
3D Shape Prisms and pyramids from nets; regular shapes	RS/E	☐		
	RS/E		☐	
Planes of symmetry	RS/E; E+			☐
Division 1 Division of whole numbers and 1st and 2nd place decimals by 2 to 10; proportion	RTN/C; AS/D; MD/D	☐		
	RTN/C, D; MD/D, E; FPR/D		☐	
	RTN/D; MD/D			☐
Angles 1 Types of angles; horizontal, vertical, parallel and perpendicular lines	PSE; ME/E, PFS/E; A/C, E		☐	
Whole numbers 2 Multiplication and division by 2 digits (pencil and paper methods)	MD/E; PFS/E; E+		☐	
Handling data 2 Trend and straight-line graphs	O/C; D/E; I/D, E	☐		
	C/E; O/D; D/E; I/D, E		☐	
Travel and curved-line graphs	D/E; I/D			☐
Detours Sets of numbers	PSE; I/E	☐		
Equalities and inequalities	FE/D		☐	
Word formulae	FE/D		☐	
Investigation	PSE		☐	

Pupil progress record: *Part 3*

Name: _____

Class: _____

Scotland
Mathematics 5–14
Attainment targets

	S	C	E

Extended context
The School Concert

PSE; AS/D, E; MD/D; RN/E; FPR/E; ME/D; T/D; PFS/E			☐

Division 2
Using a calculator; interpretation of answers

I/D; RTN/C; AS/C, D; MD/D; RN/D		☐	
RTN/D; MD/E; RN/D; E+			☐

Symmetry
Rotational symmetry

PSE; RS/D; S/E		☐	

Fractions 2
Whole number times fraction/mixed number;
fraction of a whole number

FPR/C, D, E; E+		☐	

Volume
Reading scales; volume of a cuboid
Immersion

ME/C, D, E; PFS/E		☐	
ME/C, D, E			☐

Decimals 3
Third decimal place; place value; rounding to
1st decimal place

PSE; RTN/E; AS/D, E; MD/E; RN/E; ME/E		☐	

Angles 2
Calculations; bearings; measuring and drawing
angles

A/C, D		☐	
PFS/E; A/D			☐

Time
Calendar; 12 and 24 hour times; durations

T/C, D		☐	
T/C, D			☐
PSE; T/C, D			☐

Probability
Language; outcomes; scale

E+		☐	
E+			☐

Problem solving 2
Patterns; practical investigations
Mixed strategies; elimination

PSE; PS/D, E		☐	
PSE; PS/D, E			☐
PSE; PS/D, E; PFS/E			☐

Detours
Shapes within shapes

RS/D		☐	

Overlap shapes

PSE; RS/D		☐	

Metric/Imperial relationships

D/E; I/D; ME/D			☐

Distance tables

ME/D; PFS/E			☐

© Heinemann Educational 1992

Pupil progress record: *Part 4*

Name: _____

Class: _____

Scotland Mathematics 5–14 Attainment targets	S	C	E

Percentages

Concept; using common percentages; link with fractions and decimals

	S	C	E
D/E; I/D; RTN/D; FPR/E	☐		
D/E; I/D; RTN/D, E; FPR/E; E+		☐	
PSE; I/E; RTN/D, E; FPR/E; E+			☐

Other methods 3

Multiplication and division by multiples of 10 and 100

	S	C	E
MD/C, D, E		☐	

Rate and speed

Rate per minute/second/hour

	S	C	E
T/D		☐	

Negative numbers

Concept; language; increase and decrease

	S	C	E
RTN/E; AS/E		☐	

Tessellations

Geometric shapes; patterns

	S	C	E
PSE; RS/D		☐	

Handling data 3

Designing observation sheets; class intervals

	S	C	E
C/E; O/E; D/D; I/D, E; E+		☐	

Extended context

The Field Study Week

	S	C	E
PSE; I/E; RTN/D, E; AS/C, D; MD/C, D, E; FPR/E; ME/D, E; T/C, D; PFS/E; RS/D; PM/D, E; S/D; A/D; E+		☐	

Contexts

Glenafton Weather Station

	S	C	E
PSE; D/E; ME/D; T/D; PFS/E			☐

Abermore Trout Farm

	S	C	E
I/E; MD/E; FPR/E; E+			☐

Detours

Matching shapes

	S	C	E
RS/D		☐	

Inverse operations

	S	C	E
PSE; MD/C, D		☐	

Digit sum investigation

	S	C	E
PSE			☐

Summary

Pupil progress record: *Part 1*

Name: _____

Class: _____

	Northern Ireland Common Curriculum Statements of Attainment	S	C	E
Whole numbers 1 Numbers in the environment; approximation; addition and subtraction; multiplication; division by 2 to 10	N3dh; N4agim	☐		
	P4bd; P5ab N3egh; N4acghik; N5fk; D3a		☐	
Other methods 1 Single digit calculations; associative law	N3d; N4ghm	☐		
Shape patterns Circle designs	P4ad; P5a S4b; S5d	☐		
Line symmetry; enlarging symmetrical patterns	P4ad; P5ae S4b; S5d; S6ef			☐
Decimals 1 1st and 2nd decimal place; addition and subtraction; multiplication by 2 to 10, 100, and by calculator	P3c; P5b N3beg; N4dgkl; N6a M3a	☐		
	P4b; P5b; P6ab N3beg; N4dgkl; N5fj; N6a; N7f M3ab; M4ab; M5ac D3a			☐
Length and scale Introducing the millimetre; scale drawing; drawing to scale	M3ab; M4a; M5ac	☐		
	P4b; P5a; P6ab N5i M3ab; M4a; M5ac; M6a		☐	
	M5a; M6a S4b			☐
Handling data 1 Bar graphs; mean; range; tallying and frequency tables; pie charts; bar-line graphs	D3a; D4be	☐		
	D3ac; D4ab; D5e; D6be		☐	
	P5b N4d D3c; D4a; D5e; D6b			☐
Problem solving 1 Guess and check; listing	P4d; P5a	☐		
	P4abd; P5a		☐	
	P4abd; P5af			☐
Detours Shape puzzle	P4bd S4b	☐		
Position fixing	P5b S4d	☐		
Calendar		☐		
	P4a; P5abcd			
Investigation	P5cd N4ghi A3ab		☐	
Multiples and factors	N4g A4c; A5a		☐	
Checking calculations	P5cd A4e			☐

Pupil progress record: *Part 2*

Name: _____

Class: _____

	Northern Ireland Common Curriculum Statements of Attainment	S	C	E
Decimals 2 Length; money; weight	P5b N3be; N4gkl; N5j M3ab; M5bc D3a		☐	
Other methods 2 Approximate costs	N3be; N4km; N5j		☐	
Area Rectangles; right-angled triangles; large units; composite shapes	P4d N4cg A4d M3a; M4c S4b	☐		
	P4d; P5b N4g A4d; A5e M3abc; M4c; M5a; M6c S4b		☐	
	P5b M5e			☐
Fractions 1 Equivalence; addition and subtraction of halves and quarters	N3c; N5b		☐	
3D Shape Prisms and pyramids from nets; regular shapes	P4d S4b	☐		
	S4b; S6b		☐	
Planes of symmetry	S4b; S5d			☐
Division 1 Division of whole numbers and 1st and 2nd place decimals by 2 to 10; proportion	N3beg; N4gikl D3a; D4b	☐		
	N3egi; N4gijl; N5h; N6d M5c D4b		☐	
	N3bg; N4l; N6d			☐
Angles 1 Types of angles; horizontal, vertical, parallel and perpendicular lines	P4ad; P5af M3ab; M5a S4a; S5b; S6ab		☐	
Whole numbers 2 Multiplication and division by 2 digits (pencil and paper methods)	N4c; N5fg		☐	
Handling data 2 Trend and straight-line graphs	M4b D3a; D4f	☐		
	D3a; D4f; D5af		☐	
Travel and curved-line graphs	N6e D3a; D4f			☐
Detours Sets of numbers	P4ad D3c	☐		
Equalities and inequalities	N4g A4d D4d		☐	
World formulae	A4bd			☐
Investigation	P4d; P5cd			☐

Pupil progress record: *Part 3*

Name: _____

Class: _____

	Northern Ireland Common Curriculum Statements of Attainment	S	C	E
Extended context The School Concert	P4ab; P5abf; P6ab N3begi; N4ajkln; N5hj M3abc; M4de; M5ac; M6ac			☐
Division 2 Using a calculator; interpretation of answers	P5b N3gi; N4jkln D3a; D4be		☐	
	N3bgi; N4djln M5c D3a; D4b			☐
Symmetry Rotational symmetry	P4ad S5cd; S6a			☐
Fractions 2 Whole number times fraction/mixed number; fraction of a whole number	N3c; N5h			☐
Volume Reading scales; volume of cuboid	A5e M3ab; M4acd; M5ce; M6c			☐
Immersion	M3b; M4a; M5ce			☐
Decimals 3 Third decimal place; place value; rounding to 1st decimal place	P4b; P5abe; P6ab N4adjkl; N5l; N6a A3a M3a; M5c D4b			☐
Angles 2 Calculations; bearings; measuring and drawing angles	M4d; M5d S4ac; S7b			☐
	M3a; M5ad S7b			☐
Time Calendar; 12 and 24 hour times; durations	P4d; P5b M3b; M4ae	☐		
	P5b M3b; M4ae			☐
	P5b M4ae			☐
Probability Language; outcomes; scale	D3f; D4i	☐		
	D3ef; D4hi			☐
Problem solving 2 Patterns; practical investigation Mixed strategies; elimination	A3a; A5b	☐		
	P4bd; P5abef; P6ab N5k A3a; A4bc; A5bc M3a; M6c			☐
	P5abe A3a; A4b M5a S4c			☐
Detours Shapes within shapes	S4b			☐
Overlap shapes	P4d S4b; S6a			☐
Metric/Imperial relationships	M3a; M5b D5f			☐
Distance tables	P5b M5ab			☐

Pupil progress record: *Part 4*

Name: _____

Class: _____

	Northern Ireland Common Curriculum Statements of Attainment	S	C	E
Percentages Concept; using common percentages; link with fractions and decimals	P5b N4f; N5h D3c; D6e	☐		
	N4f; N5bch; N6b D3c; D6e		☐	
	P5b N4cf; N5bch; N6 bc			☐
Other methods 3 Multiplication and division by multiples of 10 and 100	N4c; N5f	☐		
Rate and speed Rate per minute/second/hour	M3a; M4d; M5b; M6b	☐		
Negative numbers Concept; language; increase and decrease	N4e; N5i	☐		
Tessellations Geometric shapes; patterns	P4ad; P5af S6a	☐		
Handling data 3 Designing observation sheets; class intervals	D3a; D4ab; D5ad; D6b	☐		
Extended context The Field Study Week	P4d; P5abef N3eg; N4hijl; N5bch; N6 M4a; M5a; M6ab S4bc; S5d; S6f; S7b D4b	☐		
Contexts Glenafton Weather Station	P5abe M3b; M5a; M6ac D4e			☐
Abermore Trout Farm	N4jln; N5h; N6d M5c; M6b D4f; D5g			☐
Detours Matching shapes	S2a	☐		
Inverse operations	P4b; P6ab N4jl A4e			☐
Digit sum investigation	P4acd; P5ab			☐

Class progress record: *Part 1*

S ☐
C ☐
E ☐

Class: _____

Pupil	Whole numbers 1	Other methods 1	Shape patterns	Decimals 1	Length and scale	Handling data 1	Problem solving 1	Multiples and factors	Shape puzzle	Position fixing	Calendar	Investigation	Checking calculations			Comments

Detours: Calendar, Investigation, Checking calculations

Class progress record: *Part 2*

HEINEMANN MATHEMATICS 7

Detours

S ☐
C ☐
E ☐ ↓

Class:_____

Pupil	Decimals 2	Other methods 2	Area	Fractions 1	3D Shape	Division 1	Angles 1	Whole numbers 2	Handling data 2	Equalities and inequalities	Word formulae	Investigation	Sets of numbers	Comments
	☐	☐	☐☐☐	☐	☐☐	☐☐	☐	☐	☐☐☐	☐	☐	☐	☐	
	☐	☐	☐☐☐	☐	☐☐	☐☐	☐		☐☐	☐	☐	☐		
	☐	☐	☐☐		☐	☐			☐☐	☐	☐	☐		
	☐	☐	☐☐	☐			☐		☐☐	☐	☐	☐		
	☐	☐	☐☐						☐	☐	☐	☐		
	☐	☐	☐☐☐	☐	☐	☐	☐		☐☐	☐	☐	☐		
	☐	☐	☐☐	☐	☐☐	☐			☐☐	☐	☐	☐		
	☐	☐	☐	☐	☐	☐			☐	☐	☐	☐		
	☐	☐	☐☐☐	☐	☐☐	☐			☐☐	☐	☐	☐		
	☐	☐	☐☐☐	☐	☐☐	☐	☐		☐☐		☐	☐		
	☐	☐	☐☐	☐		☐	☐		☐	☐	☐	☐		
	☐	☐	☐☐☐		☐☐☐	☐	☐		☐	☐	☐	☐		
	☐	☐	☐☐☐	☐	☐☐☐	☐	☐		☐☐	☐	☐	☐		
	☐	☐	☐☐☐	☐	☐☐	☐	☐		☐☐	☐	☐	☐		
	☐	☐	☐☐☐	☐	☐☐		☐		☐☐	☐	☐	☐		
	☐	☐	☐☐☐	☐	☐☐		☐		☐☐	☐	☐	☐		

Detours

S ☐
C ☐
E ☐ ↓

Class: _____

Pupil	Extended context	Division 2	Symmetry	Fractions 2	Volume	Decimals 3	Angles 2	Time	Probability	Problem solving 2	Metric/imperial relationships	Shapes within shapes	Overlap shapes	Distance tables	Comments
	☐	☐☐	☐	☐ ☐	☐	☐ ☐	☐☐	☐☐	☐☐	☐	☐	☐ ☐		
	☐	☐☐	☐	☐	☐	☐	☐☐	☐	☐		☐ ☐	☐		
	☐	☐☐	☐ ☐	☐	☐	☐ ☐	☐☐	☐	☐		☐ ☐	☐		
	☐	☐☐	☐ ☐	☐	☐	☐	☐☐	☐	☐		☐ ☐			
	☐	☐☐	☐ ☐	☐	☐	☐	☐☐	☐☐	☐		☐ ☐	☐		
	☐	☐☐	☐ ☐	☐	☐	☐ ☐	☐☐	☐☐	☐		☐ ☐	☐		
	☐	☐☐	☐ ☐	☐	☐	☐ ☐	☐☐	☐	☐		☐ ☐	☐		
	☐	☐☐	☐ ☐	☐	☐	☐	☐☐	☐	☐		☐ ☐	☐		
	☐	☐☐	☐ ☐	☐	☐	☐ ☐	☐☐	☐	☐		☐ ☐	☐		
	☐	☐☐	☐ ☐	☐	☐	☐ ☐	☐☐	☐	☐		☐ ☐	☐		
	☐	☐☐	☐ ☐	☐	☐	☐	☐☐	☐☐	☐		☐ ☐	☐		
	☐	☐☐	☐ ☐	☐	☐	☐ ☐	☐☐	☐☐	☐		☐ ☐	☐		
	☐	☐☐	☐ ☐	☐	☐	☐	☐☐	☐☐	☐		☐ ☐	☐		
	☐	☐☐	☐ ☐	☐	☐	☐ ☐	☐☐	☐☐	☐		☐ ☐	☐		
	☐	☐☐	☐ ☐	☐	☐	☐	☐☐	☐☐	☐		☐ ☐	☐		
	☐	☐☐	☐ ☐	☐	☐	☐	☐☐	☐☐	☐		☐ ☐	☐		

© Heinemann Educational 1992

HEINEMANN MATHEMATICS 7

S ☐
C ☐ ↓
E ☐

Class: _____

Pupil

Percentages
Other methods 3
Rate and speed
Negative numbers
Tessellations
Handling data 3
Extended context
Contexts
Inverse operations
Matching shapes
Digit sum investigation

Detours

Comments

HEINEMANN MATHEMATICS 7
REVISED NATIONAL CURRICULUM SUMMARY CHART

	Using and Applying			Number			Algebra		Shape, Space and Measures			Handling Data	
Programme of Study	2	3	4	2	3	4	2	3	2	3	4	2	3
Whole Numbers 1	a	ad		a	abcef	a						a	
Other methods 1			a		bf								
Shape patterns	c	ce							abc	b			
Decimals 1				ab	ce	ab					ab		
Length and scale	bd	c							b	d	ab		
Handling data 1					d							abcdefg	
Problem solving 1	ac												
Detours	ac	acd	b	a	a	c	b			a			
Decimals 2		b				ab					ab		
Other methods 2					cf								
Area											ad		
Fractions 1				b	c								
3D shape									abc				
Division 1					bce	a							
Angles 1	abc	abc							d				
Whole numbers 2					b								
Handling data 2							c				d	acf	
Detours		abd	bd	a	a			b				c	
Extended context	abc	cd			c	ab				d			
Division 2					bce	bd						ad	
Symmetry									c	b			
Fractions 2					ce	ab							
Volume											abd		
Decimals 3				a		d					ab		
Angles 2									d	a			
Time			a			b					a		
Probability													abde
Problem solving 2	abc		d				b			d			
Detours		bd							ab		a		
Percentages				b	cd	b						c	
Other methods 3					bc	b							
Rate and speed						ad					c		
Negative numbers				b	c								
Tessellations	ce								ab	bc			
Handling data 3		e										acef	
Extended context	acd	b	e	b	cd	b		b	bcd	ad	a		
Contexts		bcd			c	ab					c	cf	
Detours	bc		b	a	c				ab				
Summary	abcd	abcde	abde	ab	abcdef	abcd	bc	b	abcd	abcd	abcd	abcdefg	abde

T29

HEINEMANN MATHEMATICS 7   MATHEMATICS 5–14 SUMMARY CHART

Level D / Level E

	Information Handling					Number, Money & Measurement											Shape, Position & Movement			
	PSE	C	O	D	I	RTN	M	AS	MD	RN	FPR	PS	FE	ME	T	PFS	RS	PM	S	A

Whole numbers 1
Other methods 1
Shape patterns
Decimals 1
Length & scale
Handling data 1
Problem solving 1
Detours

Decimals 2
Other methods 2
Area
Fractions 1
3D Shape
Division 1
Angles 1
Whole numbers 2
Handling data 2
Detours

Extended context
Division 2
Symmetry
Fractions 2
Volume
Decimals 3
Angles 2
Time
Probability
Problem solving 2
Detours

Percentages
Other methods 3
Rate & speed
Negative numbers
Tessellations
Handling data 3
Extended context
Contexts
Detours

Summary

HEINEMANN MATHEMATICS 7   COMMON CURRICULUM SUMMARY CHART

	Processes in Mathematics			Number			Algebra			Measures			Shape and Space			Handling Data		
	4	5	6	4	5	6	4	5	6	4	5	6	4	5	6	4	5	6
Whole numbers 1	□	□	▓	□	□	▓	▓	▓	▓	▓	▓	▓	▓	▓	▓	▓	▓	▓
Other methods 1	▓	▓	▓	▓	▓	▓	▓	▓	▓	▓	▓	▓	▓	▓	▓	▓	▓	▓
Shape patterns	▓	□	▓	▓	▓	▓	▓	▓	▓	▓	▓	▓	▓	▓	▓	▓	▓	▓
Decimals 1	▓	□	▓	□	□	□	▓	▓	▓	▓	□	▓	▓	▓	▓	▓	▓	▓
Length & scale	▓	□	▓	▓	▓	▓	▓	▓	▓	□	□	□	▓	▓	▓	▓	▓	▓
Handling data 1	▓	□	▓	▓	▓	▓	▓	▓	▓	▓	▓	▓	▓	▓	▓	□	□	□
Problem solving 1	□	□	▓	□	▓	▓	▓	□	▓	▓	▓	▓	▓	▓	▓	▓	▓	▓
Detours	▓	▓	▓	▓	□	▓	▓	□	▓	▓	▓	▓	▓	▓	▓	▓	▓	▓
Decimals 2	▓	▓	▓	□	□	□	▓	▓	▓	▓	□	▓	▓	▓	▓	▓	▓	▓
Other methods 2	▓	▓	▓	□	□	□	▓	□	▓	▓	▓	▓	▓	▓	▓	▓	▓	▓
Area	▓	▓	▓	▓	▓	▓	▓	▓	▓	□	□	▓	▓	▓	▓	▓	▓	▓
Fractions 1	▓	□	▓	□	□	▓	▓	▓	▓	▓	▓	▓	▓	▓	▓	▓	▓	▓
3D Shape	▓	□	▓	▓	▓	▓	▓	▓	▓	▓	▓	▓	□	□	□	▓	▓	▓
Division 1	□	□	▓	□	□	▓	▓	▓	▓	▓	▓	▓	▓	▓	▓	▓	▓	▓
Angles 1	▓	▓	▓	▓	▓	▓	▓	▓	▓	▓	▓	▓	□	□	□	▓	▓	▓
Whole numbers 2	▓	□	▓	□	□	□	▓	▓	▓	▓	▓	▓	▓	▓	▓	▓	▓	▓
Handling data 2	▓	□	▓	▓	▓	□	▓	□	▓	□	▓	▓	▓	▓	▓	□	□	□
Detours	▓	▓	▓	▓	□	▓	▓	□	▓	▓	▓	▓	▓	▓	▓	▓	▓	▓
Extended context	□	□	▓	□	□	▓	▓	▓	▓	▓	□	▓	▓	▓	▓	▓	▓	▓
Division 2	▓	▓	▓	□	□	▓	▓	▓	▓	▓	▓	▓	▓	▓	▓	▓	▓	▓
Symmetry	▓	▓	▓	▓	▓	▓	▓	▓	▓	▓	▓	▓	□	□	□	▓	▓	▓
Fractions 2	▓	▓	▓	□	□	▓	▓	▓	▓	▓	▓	▓	▓	▓	▓	▓	▓	▓
Volume	▓	▓	▓	▓	▓	▓	▓	□	▓	□	□	▓	▓	▓	▓	▓	▓	▓
Decimals 3	▓	▓	▓	□	□	▓	▓	▓	▓	▓	□	▓	▓	▓	▓	▓	▓	▓
Angles 2	▓	▓	▓	▓	▓	▓	▓	▓	▓	▓	▓	▓	□	□	□	▓	▓	▓
Time	▓	□	▓	▓	▓	▓	▓	▓	▓	□	□	□	▓	▓	▓	▓	▓	▓
Probability	▓	▓	▓	▓	▓	▓	▓	▓	▓	▓	▓	▓	▓	▓	▓	□	□	□
Problem solving 2	□	□	▓	□	▓	▓	▓	□	▓	▓	▓	▓	▓	▓	▓	▓	▓	▓
Detours	▓	▓	▓	▓	□	▓	▓	□	▓	▓	▓	▓	▓	▓	▓	▓	▓	▓
Percentages	▓	□	▓	□	□	▓	▓	▓	▓	▓	▓	▓	▓	▓	▓	▓	□	□
Other methods 3	▓	▓	▓	□	□	□	▓	□	▓	▓	▓	▓	▓	▓	▓	▓	▓	▓
Rate & speed	▓	□	▓	▓	▓	▓	▓	▓	▓	□	□	□	▓	▓	▓	▓	▓	▓
Negative numbers	▓	▓	▓	□	□	▓	▓	▓	▓	▓	▓	▓	▓	▓	▓	▓	▓	▓
Tessellations	▓	▓	▓	▓	▓	▓	▓	▓	▓	▓	▓	▓	□	□	□	▓	▓	▓
Handling data 3	□	□	▓	▓	▓	▓	▓	▓	▓	▓	▓	▓	▓	▓	▓	□	□	□
Extended context	□	□	▓	□	□	▓	▓	▓	▓	▓	□	▓	▓	▓	▓	▓	▓	▓
Contexts	□	□	▓	▓	▓	▓	▓	▓	▓	▓	□	▓	▓	▓	▓	▓	▓	▓
Detours	▓	▓	▓	▓	□	▓	▓	□	▓	▓	▓	▓	▓	▓	▓	▓	▓	▓
Summary	□	□	□	□	□	□	□	□	▓	□	□	□	□	□	□	□	□	□

HEINEMANN MATHEMATICS 7

Teaching Notes

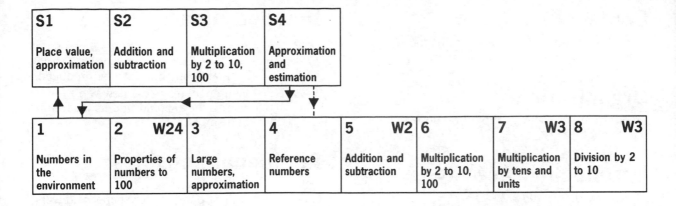

S1	S2	S3	S4
Place value, approximation	Addition and subtraction	Multiplication by 2 to 10, 100	Approximation and estimation

1	2 W24	3	4	5 W2	6	7 W3	8 W3
Numbers in the environment	Properties of numbers to 100	Large numbers, approximation	Reference numbers	Addition and subtraction	Multiplication by 2 to 10, 100	Multiplication by tens and units	Division by 2 to 10

CONTENT AND DEVELOPMENT

Core

The whole number work covered by pupils should have included: place value to millions, approximation to the nearest 10, 100 and 1000, multiplication by tens and units, 100 and 1000, division by one- and two-digit numbers.

In *Whole numbers 1*, this work is consolidated and extended to cover:

- approximation to the nearest 10, 100, 1000
- reference numbers
- addition and subtraction (up to four digits)
- multiplication by 2 to 10, 100
- multiplication by two-digit numbers
- division by 2 to 10.

Much of the work is in the context of a mail-order catalogue.

Support

Support pages S1–S4 provide an easier lead-in to some of the Core Textbook pages. On completion of the Support pages pupils could attempt Core Textbook page 4 as this refers to the Goodies catalogue which is an integral part of the Core Textbook.

National Curriculum (England and Wales)

UA2a, 3ad
N2a, 3abcef, 4a
HD2a

Mathematics 5–14 (Scotland)

PSE
RTN/C1, D, D1, D2
AS/C3, C4, D1, D2, E1, E2, E3
MD/C2, C3, C4, D1
RN/C1, D1, E

RELATED ACTIVITIES

Encourage pupils to bring in examples of numbers that they see around them. These could come from a variety of sources such as newspapers and labels for food or clothes. Pupils could then make a wall display of the different types of numbers that they have collected. A separate section could include examples of numbers which have been rounded.

EQUIPMENT

Calculator, scissors, coloured pencils, cards from W24.
For the Introductory activities: card.

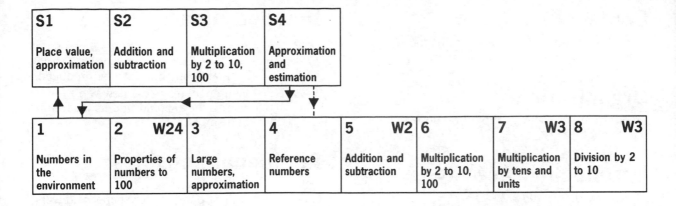

WHOLE NUMBERS 1

PART ONE

1

Whole
numbers 1:
Numbers
in the
environment

UA3d/3
N2a/3

RTN/D1

Content

- Interpretation of written information
- Reading and writing whole numbers.

Organisation

The Introductory activity should be done before pupils attempt Q4.

Introductory activity

Number classification
Before pupils attempt Q4, discuss with them the different types of numbers used in the newspaper extract. Pupils could be asked to classify the numbers under the following headings:

- measures such as weight (109 kg), length (23 cm) and time (10 min)
- amounts of money (£200), people (700), objects (25 000)
- an order (1st)
- a reference (GT4).

Detailed notes

Q1, 2 Encourage pupils to write the meaning of the numbers in their own words. A variety of acceptable answers may be produced.

Q2h Octocentenary may be a new word for pupils and they should find its meaning for themselves.

Additional activities

1 Number news
Give each group of pupils a newspaper and ask them to make a list of ten numbers used in it and state what each refers to. Groups could compare their numbers and meanings.

2 Computerised newspaper
Computer programs are available which allow pupils to lay out the front page of a newspaper. A page could be made up using the best stories produced by the pupils in Q4.

Equipment

None.

2

W24

Whole
numbers 1:
Properties of
numbers to
100

N2a, 3a/4

PSE
MD/D1
RN/D1

Content

- Approximation to the nearest 10
- Interpretation of information
- Problem solving – working systematically, guess and check.

Introductory activities

1 Number classification
Pupils may require some revise of the following terms: digit, odd, even, multiple, divisible. The following activity could be used.

Ask pupils to give you ten numbers less than 100. These numbers could then be categorised under various headings which have been displayed in advance on the blackboard or overhead projector. For example,

15, 18, 32, 45, 3,
78, 87, 64, 26, 41

can be
categorised as

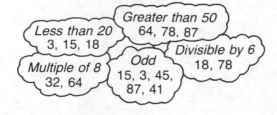

2 Approximation to the nearest 10
The number 37 can be approximated by drawing a number line marked with the numbers 30 and 40 as shown.

Discuss which number is midway between 30 and 40 and mark it as shown.

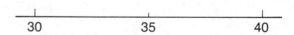

The number 37 can be placed by deciding whether it is bigger or smaller than 35.

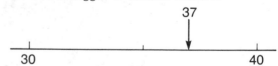

37 is nearer to 40 than 30.
37 is 40 to the nearest ten.
Repeat this for other numbers, for example: 23, 38, 56, 14.

Detailed notes

Q8b The longest domino chain used 10 coupons.

Equipment

Scissors, cards from W24.

Introducing the Goodies catalogue

Core Textbook pages 4 to 8 refer to a mail-order catalogue from the imaginary firm Goodies. Five pages from this catalogue (Pages 69 to 73) are reproduced at the end of the Core Textbook. The contents of these pages are:

Catalogue Page 69 Sports equipment
Catalogue Page 70 Casual clothing
Catalogue Page 71 Footwear and sportswear
Catalogue Page 72 TV, stereo, cameras, films, records, tapes
Catalogue Page 73 Personal gifts.

The catalogue pages do not contain questions but provide a context for a variety of work in the Core Textbook. As some pupils may not have had any experience of buying through a mail-order catalogue it is important that the teacher discusses what is involved with them and allows pupils to become familiar with the catalogue pages. Some Textbook pages require frequent reference to the catalogue pages and it is suggested that pupils work in pairs where one has the page open at the questions and the other has the book open at the appropriate catalogue page.

3

Whole
numbers 1:
Large
numbers,
approxi-
mation

N2a/4

RTN/D2
RN/D1, E

Content

- Approximation to the nearest 100, 1000
- Interpretation of information.

Introductory activities

1 The nearest thousand
Revise or introduce approximation to the nearest
thousand by using a number line. For example,
9265 can be approximated to the nearest thousand
as follows.

Draw a number line marked with the numbers
9000 and 10 000 as shown.

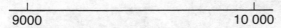

Discuss which number is midway between 9000
and 10 000 and mark it as shown.

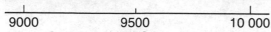

The number 9265 can be placed by deciding
whether it is bigger or smaller than 9500.

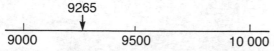

The number 9265 is nearer to 9000 than 10 000.
9265 is 9000 to the nearest thousand.
Repeat this for other numbers, for example: 3800,
5300, 7980, 1320, 6515.

2 The nearest hundred
Use a similar approach to that in Introductory
activity 1. For example, 3423 can be approximated
to the nearest hundred as follows.

Draw a number line marked in hundreds and with
the numbers 3000 and 4000 on it as shown.

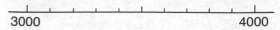

Discuss the position of 3423 between 3400 and
3500 and mark the position of the number midway
between them.

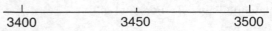

The number 3423 can now be placed on the
number line.

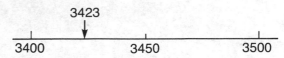

The number 3423 is nearer to 3400 than 3500.
3423 is 3400 to the nearest hundred.
Repeat this for other numbers, for example: 3580,
5265, 1830, 2213.

Equipment

None.

4

Whole
numbers 1:
Reference
numbers

UA3ad/
4 → 5
HD2a/4

RTN/D

Content

- Interpretation of codes and reference
  numbers from a catalogue.

Introductory activities

1 Reference numbers
This page could be introduced by a class
discussion about reference numbers, such as

Dates of birth
Driving license number
Clothes sizes

Class code
Car number plates
National Insurance
number.

The meaning of different parts of a reference
number could also be discussed. For example, in
car number plate A533 BSX, the letter A refers to
its year of manufacture.

2 Catalogue reference numbers
Ensure that pupils know how to interpret the
Goodies reference numbers by discussing the
numbers used on each catalogue page. For
example, SE 6901 is Sports Equipment, item 1 on
Catalogue page 69, a football.

Detailed notes

Q3, 6 The items in these questions do not
appear in the Goodies catalogue. The
reference numbers in Q3 must be four
digits, for example, the number for Q3b is
2604 and not 264.

Equipment

None.

5

W2

Whole
numbers 1:
Addition and
subtraction

N3e/3;
3b/4
HD2a/4

PSE
AS/E1, E2,
E3

Content

- Addition and subtraction of two-, three- and
  four-digit whole numbers
- Problem solving – working systematically,
  guess and check.

Detailed notes

Q1, 6 Encourage pupils to work systematically.
For example, in Q6 subtract 5 from each
of the other numbers then subtract 94
from each of the other bigger numbers
and so on. The pupils are then more
likely to find all ten possible calculations.

W2, Q2, col. 5 Some pupils may require help to
complete this column. The pupils should
find that only four types need re-ordering
because orders have only to be made
when the stock falls below 100.

W2, Q5, 7 A calculator is recommended for these
questions.

W2, Q7 Some pupils may need help in
interpreting the 'Change in sales'.

Q9 Uses the answers from Q8.

Equipment

Calculator.

Content

- Interpretation of information in a catalogue
- Multiplication by 2 to 10, 100.

Introductory activity

Multiplication by a single digit
Ensure pupils are familiar with the Catalogue page before using it to find the prices for Q1. Revise multiplication by a single digit with examples such as the following:

(a) 5 small stickers at 32p = £1·60

$$\begin{array}{r} 32 \\ \times 5 \\ \hline 160 \end{array}$$

(b) 7 silver name pendants at £24 = £168

$$\begin{array}{r} 24 \\ \times 7 \\ \hline 168 \end{array}$$

(c) 28 albums at £8 = £224

$$\begin{array}{r} 28 \\ \times 8 \\ \hline 224 \end{array}$$

(d) 3 medium T-shirts at £3·49 = £10·47

$$\begin{array}{r} 349 \\ \times 3 \\ \hline 1047 \end{array}$$

Pupils should work in pence to avoid decimal calculations but should express their answers in £.

Detailed notes

Q2, 3, 4 The cost of special notices depends on the number and colour of the letters.

Q5 If necessary, remind pupils of the rule for multiplication by 100: 'move the digits two places to the left'.

Equipment
None.

Content

- Multiplication of a two-digit whole number by a two-digit whole number
- Interpretation of information
- Problem solving – working systematically, guess and check.

Organisation

Decide to what extent you wish a calculator to be used for the work on this page.

Detailed notes

Q2 Pupils should realize that message (a) is in large print while the other two (which have more than 15 letters each) are in small print.

Q4 Some pupils may need help to find items from their reference numbers.

Equipment
Calculator.

7
W3
Whole numbers 1: Multiplication by tens and units

UA2a/5
N3e/3; 3ab/4
HD2a/4

PSE
MD/C3, C4

Content

- Interpretation of information in a catalogue
- Division of two- and three-digit whole numbers by whole numbers from 2 to 10.

Detailed notes

Q1e Pupils should change £2·03 into 203p to give a whole number division.

Q3 If necessary, remind pupils that these prices include the cost of lettering. By adding the cost of lettering for each person to the price of the item, it is possible to decide who purchased each item.

Equipment
Calculator.

S1
Whole numbers 1:
Place value
approximation

N2a/4

RTN/C1
RN/C1, D1

Content

- Reading, writing and ordering whole numbers
- Place value to thousands
- Approximation to the nearest 100, 1000.

Introductory activities

The context of the page could be set by finding some appropriate numbers in a newspaper. These numbers could be used in each of the following activities.

1 Place values
Revise place values with pupils by asking them to write out a number as follows:

362 is 3 hundreds, 6 tens and 2 units *or*
36 tens and 2 units.

Pupils could then be asked to write the following numbers (or numbers found in the newspaper) in the same way: 573, 805, 34, 930, 1730.

They could then write out each number in words. This gives an opportunity for the language in *figures* and in *words* to be highlighted.

Then ask pupils to give the value of a digit in a number. For example, the value of the digit 3 in 43, 235, 1375, 3205.

2 Approximation to the nearest hundred, thousand.
The Introductory activities for Core Textbook page 3 explain a possible approach for approximating to the nearest hundred and thousand.

Detailed notes

Q4 A bundle is 100 papers.

Equipment

None.

Content

- Addition and subtraction of two- and three-digit numbers
- Ordering whole numbers.

Introductory activities

You may wish to revise the following before pupils proceed with the work of this page.

1 Addition of one- and two-digit numbers
Pupils may need to be reminded of place value when setting out their calculations.

$$\begin{array}{r} 32 \\ 5 \\ 17 \\ \underline{54} \\ \scriptstyle 1 \end{array}$$

2 Subtraction
Some pupils may require extra practice examples.

$$\begin{array}{r} {}^5\!\!\!\not6{}^12 \\ -4\ 8 \\ \hline 1\ 4 \end{array}$$

Equipment

None.

S3
Whole numbers 1:
Multiplication
by 2 to 10,
100

N3ab/4

MD/C3, D1

Content

- Multiplication of two- and three-digit numbers by a single-digit number
- Ordering whole numbers.

Introductory activity

Dominoes
Ensure that pupils are familiar with the game by letting them play a game of dominoes with either a traditional set or one of the many mathematical ones available. You could also construct your own set of dominoes such as those shown opposite based on the multiplication tables.

Detailed notes

Q1 The orientation in which the matching product is written does not matter.

Q2 Pupils may need help with the initial colouring and move. Not all answers need be found, only those on the 'path'.

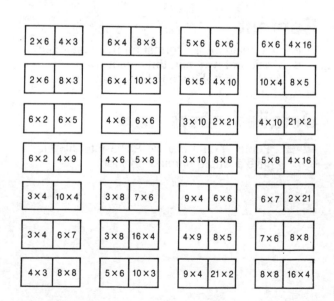

Equipment

Coloured pencil.
For the Introductory activity: card.

Content

- Approximation to the nearest 100
- Use of estimation to check the validity of addition calculations.

Introductory activity

Designer clothes

Introduce the context of this page with a class discussion about designer clothes. Establish that the high prices of these clothes could arise because of the material used, because of their uniqueness, because they are hand-made and not mass produced, etc.

Detailed notes

Q3a Some pupils may need to set out a calculation in order to estimate these totals. For example:

Designer clothes	£500
	£300
	£400
	£1200

Q3b Pupils should check their answers by finding the exact totals.

Equipment

None.

OTHER METHODS 1

10	11
Single-digit calculations	Using the Associative Laws

CONTENT AND DEVELOPMENT

Core

The *Other methods* sections present alternative approaches to computation. *Other methods 1* covers:

- approximation to the nearest 100, 1000
- mental addition and subtraction of whole numbers
- estimation of the answers to addition and subtraction problems by approximating to the nearest 100, 1000
- informal study of the Associative Laws for addition and multiplication.

Other methods 2 (on pages 41–42 of these notes) contains work on the estimation of money totals.

National Curriculum (England and Wales)

UA4a
N3bf

Mathematics 5–14 (Scotland)

PSE
AS/C3, D1, E3
MD/D1
RN/D1, E

EQUIPMENT

Calculator, card, scissors.

Content

- Approximation to the nearest 100, 1000
- Mental addition and subtraction of whole numbers
- Estimation of addition and subtraction problems by approximating to the nearest 100, 1000.

Introductory activities

1 Approximation to the nearest hundred, thousand
Some revision of approximating to the nearest hundred or thousand may be necessary (see Introductory activities for Core Textbook page 3.)

2 Approximate costs
Ask pupils to find the total cost of these two items:

Big screen TV £768

Portable video £135

Pupils should first estimate by rounding to the nearest hundred and then do the calculation mentally as shown:

768 is about 8 hundred.
135 is about 1 hundred.

8 hundred and 1 hundred
is 9 hundred.
The total cost is about £900.

Detailed notes

Q4 The answers exceed 10 hundreds and may cause difficulty for some pupils.

Equipment
Calculator.

Content

- Mental addition of two-digit numbers
- Multiplication of a two-digit by a single-digit number
- Informal study of the Associative Laws for addition and multiplication.

Introductory activities

1 Mental addition
Pupils can be challenged to add mentally numbers such as 6 + 35 + 4. The different ways in which the pupils calculate the answer should be identified and discussed. Adding 6 and 4 to make 10 should be seen as a particularly easy method. Pupils can then be asked to find the total of each of the following and a similar discussion can take place for each.

7 + 16 + 3   14 + 8 + 6
15 + 30 + 5   12 + 6 + 18 + 4

2 Mental multiplication
The procedure above for mental addition could be used for examples such as

8 × 2 × 5   100 × 4 × 7
7 × 10 × 7   8 × 20 × 3

and the easiest order of each discussed.

11
Other methods 1: Using the Associative Laws

UA4a/5
N3b/4

PSE
AS/D1
MD/D1

Detailed notes

Q10 This question should show pupils that the order cannot be changed in subtraction and division.

Equipment
Card, scissors.

SHAPE PATTERNS

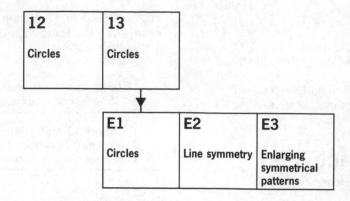

CONTENT AND DEVELOPMENT

Core

Previous 2D shape work should have introduced the circle and other mathematical shapes and dealt with line symmetry.

This *Shape patterns* section covers:

■ revision of centre, radius and circumference
■ practical work using compasses to make circle designs.

Extension

This should be done on completion of Core Textbook page 13. It contains

■ line symmetry
■ enlargement of symmetrical patterns.

National Curriculum (England and Wales)

UA2c, 3ce
SM2abc, 3b

Mathematics 5–14 (Scotland)

RS/C2, D4
S/D1, D2
E+

RELATED ACTIVITIES

The design work can be related to other areas of the curriculum and pupils should be encouraged to make circle designs of their own without having to relate them to mathematics.

EQUIPMENT

Ruler, compasses, card, white paper plates, coloured pencils, scissors, $\frac{1}{2}$ cm or 1 cm squared paper, plain paper, glue, mirror.

Content

■ Construction of circle designs and patterns.

Introductory activities

Discuss various methods of drawing circles.

1 Drawing round a template
Use various upturned objects as templates. The term circumference should be used to describe the boundary line.

2 Using string and chalk or pencil
Use a looped piece of string and chalk (or pencil) as shown.

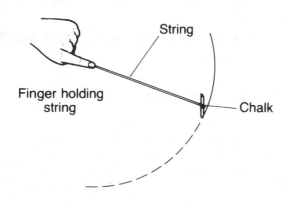

Finger holding string

String

Chalk

Highlight the terms:
■ centre (finger or drawing pin)
■ circumference (path traced out by the chalk or pencil)
■ radius (length of string between finger and chalk).

3 Using compasses
Pupils should
■ know that when the compasses are closed the pencil point and the steel point should be aligned

■ be shown how to set compasses in order to draw a circle of a given radius
■ be given practice in drawing circles with specific radii.

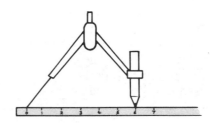

Detailed notes

Q1 Some pupils may have difficulty drawing circles with a radius as small as 2 cm.

Q4 A more difficult question involving two sets of concentric circles. Radii of 2, 4, 6, 8 and 10 cm will produce this effect on an A4 sheet of paper.

Q5 Pupils should be encouraged to make designs and patterns of their own.

Equipment

Compasses, ruler, coloured pencils, plain paper.

Content

■ Construction of circle designs and patterns.

Introductory activity

Finding the centre of a circle
Various ways of finding the centre should be discussed. For example:
■ Fold a circular piece of paper (filter paper) in half, open it out and fold again in the opposite direction. Where the diameters cross is the centre.
■ Move a ruler across the circle until the largest length between the two points on the circumference is found. This length is the diameter and the mid point is the centre of the circle.

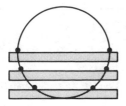

■ To find the centre of a paper plate with a ridged edge, count the ridges and draw a dotted line as shown. The mid point of this line gives the centre of the circle.

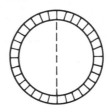

Detailed notes

Q3 The centres of the circles lie on a straight line.

Equipment

Compasses, ruler, coloured pencils, white paper plate, cardboard.

E1
Shape
patterns:
Circles

SM2ab/
4 → 5

RS/C2, D4
S/D2

Content

- Construction of regular octagons, regular hexagons, 8-pointed and 6-pointed stars from circles
- Making designs from circles.

Detailed notes

Q1 The regular octagon may be new to some pupils.

Q2 Pupils could cut out their 8-pointed stars and make a wall display.

Q4a The letters A to F appear in the first design as a reminder of the method used in Q3.

Q4b The pupil's own designs or the designs used in Q4(a) could be used.

Additional activity

Star of David
Pupils could investigate why the six-pointed star shape is known as the Star of David. It is used as a symbol of Judaism and of the State of Israel.

Equipment

Compasses, ruler, card, scissors, coloured pencils.

E2
Shape
patterns:
Line
symmetry

SM2bc,
3b/5

S/D1, D2

Content

- Completing shape patterns with given lines of symmetry
- Identifying and naming lines of symmetry on shape patterns.

Introductory activity

Lines of symmetry
Using a squared grid on a blackboard, wall chart or overhead projector discuss the following principles of grid symmetry in relation to each of these diagrams:

- a line of symmetry can be thought of as a 'mirror line'
- coloured squares are 'reflected' in the 'mirror line'
- a coloured square and its reflection lie on a line which is at right angles to the 'mirror line' and are the same distance from it.

b – blue   r – red   y – yellow

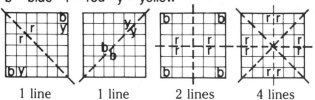

| 1 line | 1 line | 2 lines | 4 lines |

Detailed notes

Q1 The numbers 1, 2 and 3 refer to the colours of the pencils, for example, colour 1 might be red, colour 2 yellow and colour 3 blue.

Q2 Pupils should be aware of the significance of the word 'only'. Their patterns should not have other lines of symmetry.

Q3 A brief explanation of how to name a line of symmetry may be required.

Q4 Pattern 3 has no line of symmetry.

Equipment

Coloured pencils, $\frac{1}{2}$ cm or 1 cm squared paper. A mirror may be useful for some pupils.

E3
Shape
patterns:
Enlarging
symmetrical
patterns

UA2c/
5 → 6
SM2bc,
3b/5

S/D1, D2,
E+

Content

- Construction of shape patterns with four lines of symmetry
- Construction of equilateral triangles from circles
- Enlargement of shape patterns
- Identification of lines of symmetry in shape patterns.

Organisation

Group work is essential. For Q1 to Q4 a group of six has the advantage that each pupil, as well as designing an individual pattern, can be responsible for enlarging one of the six pieces of the chosen pattern.

Additional activity

Further enlargement
More than one of the patterns designed in Q1 could be chosen for enlargement.

Equipment

1 cm squared paper, plain paper, compasses, coloured pencils, glue.

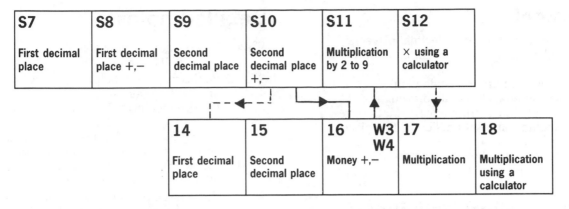

S7	S8	S9	S10	S11	S12
First decimal place	First decimal place +,−	Second decimal place	Second decimal place +,−	Multiplication by 2 to 9	× using a calculator

14	15	16 W3 W4	17	18
First decimal place	Second decimal place	Money +,−	Multiplication	Multiplication using a calculator

CONTENT AND DEVELOPMENT

Core

Previous decimal work should have covered place value to hundredths, addition and subtraction of two-place decimals, multiplication and division of two-place decimals by 2 to 10 and also by two-digit whole numbers using the calculator, multiplication of two-place decimals by 100, interpretation of a calculator display in context, approximation to the nearest whole number.

In *Decimals 1*, some of the above work is consolidated and multiplication is extended to include multiplying by three-digit whole numbers using the calculator. The section covers:

- place value to hundredths
- addition and subtraction of two-place decimals
- multiplication by 2 to 10 and 100
- multiplication by two- and three-digit whole numbers using the calculator.

The division of decimals is covered in these notes in *Division 1* (see pages 55–59) and *Division 2* (see pages 77–80). Further work on two-place decimals is covered in *Decimals 2* (pages 38–40). The third decimal place and also approximation to the first decimal place is introduced in *Decimals 3* (pages 91–96).

Support

S7 to S10 provide parallel material to Core Textbook pages 14 and 15 and also lead-in material to Core Textbook page 16.

Less able pupils could omit the work on multiplication at this stage and return to it when the other members of the class are attempting the work of *Decimals 3*. It is possible for these pupils to use S11 and S12 as lead-in material to Core Textbook pages 17 and 18.

National Curriculum (England and Wales)

N2ab, 3ce, 4ab
SM4ab

Mathematics 5–4 (Scotland)

PSE
RTN/D3, D4
AS/D, D2, D3
MD/D2, D3, D4
ME/D1
PFS/E3

RELATED ACTIVITIES

Decimal research
Pupils could make a display of decimal numbers found in everyday life. Information will be found in other subject areas, newspapers and magazines, labels and packaging, and so on.

EQUIPMENT

Ruler, calculator, coloured pencils.
For the Introductory activities: measuring equipment such as metre tapes and weighing scales which are marked in tenths.

14

Decimals 1:
First decimal
place

N2ab,
3c/4 → 5

RTN/D3
AS/D2
ME/D1
PFS/E3

Content

- Concept of the first decimal place
- Relationship between common fractions and decimals
- Interpretation of a scale plan
- Measurement of scale drawing and calculation of true length
- Addition and subtraction of first place decimals
- Relationship between metres and centimetres.

Introductory activities

1 Revision of tenths using a grid
Draw a grid like this.

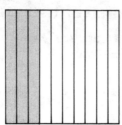

In discussion with pupils establish that
- there are ten equal strips in the whole square
- the area of each strip is one tenth or $\frac{1}{10}$ or 0·1 of the whole square
- the shaded area can be recorded as 3 tenths or $\frac{3}{10}$ or 0·3
- the area which is not shaded can be recorded as 7 tenths or $\frac{7}{10}$ or 0·7.

Pupils should become familiar with the different methods of recording.

In the same way use diagrams like these to show that the total shaded area is

2 units and 3 tenths *or*
$2\frac{3}{10}$ *or*
2·3 *or*
23 tenths.

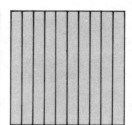
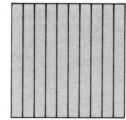
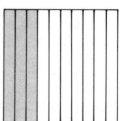

2 Revision of tenths using a number line
Draw a number line like this.

In discussion with pupils establish that
- each unit is divided into ten equal small intervals
- each small interval represents one tenth or $\frac{1}{10}$ or 0·1 of a unit.

Pupils should be able to state which decimal fraction is represented by any mark, and to show where a given decimal fraction would lie on the number line. Examples could include: 0·2, 1·5, 2·0, 2·4, 3·7, 5·1

Detailed notes

 Pupils should know that
$\frac{1}{2} = \frac{5}{10} = 0\cdot5$, $\frac{1}{5} = \frac{2}{10} = 0\cdot2$

Q3 Pupils may need help to interpret the plan and/or the scale. Ask them initially to find the distance from The Cross to each of the red dots: The Cross to the School measures 5 cm, 5 × 0·1 km = 0·5 km. Distances such as from the School to the Playing Fields can then be found by addition: 0·5 km + 0·6 km = 1·1 km.

Q5 Conversion between metres and centimetres is required.

Equipment
Ruler.

Content

- Place value to hundredths, ordering
- Relationship between common fractions and decimals
- Interpretation of a scale marked in hundredths
- Relationship between metres and centimetres.

Introductory activities

1 Revision of hundredths using a grid
Draw a grid like this.

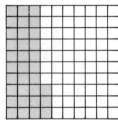

In discussion with pupils establish that
- there are 100 equal small squares in the whole square
- the area of each small square is one hundredth or $\frac{1}{100}$ or 0·01 of the whole square
- the shaded area is 34 hundredths or $\frac{34}{100}$ or 0·34
- the area which is not shaded is 66 hundredths or $\frac{66}{100}$ or 0·66.

Pupils should realise from the diagram that 34 hundredths is also 3 tenths and 4 hundredths.

In the same way use diagrams like these to show that the shaded area is

2 units and 34 hundredths *or*
$2\frac{34}{100}$ *or*
2·34 *or*
234 hundredths.

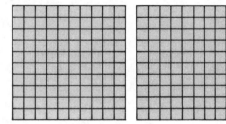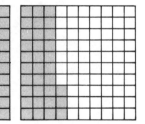

2 Revision of hundredths using a number line
Draw a number line like this.

| 2 | 2·1 | 2·2 | 2·3 | 2·4 | 2·5 | 2·6 | 2·7 | 2·8 | 2·9 | 3 |

In discussion with pupils establish that
- each unit is divided into 100 equal small intervals
- each small interval represents one hundredth or $\frac{1}{100}$ or 0·01 of a unit.

Pupils should be able to state which decimal fraction is represented by any mark, and to show where given decimal fractions would lie on the number line. Examples could include: 1·68, 1·5 or 1·50, 1·05, 1·0 or 1·00, 0·9, 0·09.

3 Length
Revise the use of decimal notation in length. For example: 0·56 m means 56 cm, 2·34 m means 2 m and 34 cm or 234 cm.

Detailed notes

Q5c Pupils should know that $\frac{1}{4} = 0.25$, $\frac{3}{4} = 0.75$

Q6 Conversion between metres and centimetres is necessary.

N2ab/
4 → 5
SM4a/5

RTN/D3, D4

Equipment
None.

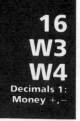

16
W3
W4
Decimals 1:
Money +,−

N3e/4;
3c/5

PSE
RTN/D4
AS/D2, D3

Content

- Addition and subtraction of two-place decimals in money
- Interpretation of information in written, tabular and diagrammatic forms
- Problem solving: working backwards, trial and error, listing.

Organisation

See page 3 of these notes for information on the use of the Goodies catalogue.

The work on this page can be carried out using either paper and pencil or calculator techniques. The pupils could first do the questions using the paper and pencil techniques, and then check their answers using a calculator.

Introductory activities

1 Money and the calculator
Ensure that pupils can interpret a calculator display in the context of money, for example:

3.45 as £3·45 *or* £3 and 45p

9.2 as £9·20

0.47 as 47p   **0.3** as 30p

0.03 as 3p   **3.** as £3

Detailed notes

Q4 The order forms may need some discussion.

Q8 Various combinations of items are possible. Answers could be checked by a partner. It would be possible to limit the choices to include only one of any particular item or size of item.

Q9 Involves interpretation of '20 weeks at'.

Ask pupils to enter money in pounds in a calculator, for example: £13·65, £13·00, 65p, 5p.

In discussion highlight that in many calculators the zeroes in 13.00 disappear when the = key is pressed.
Some pupils may enter 5. or 0.5 instead of 0.05 for 5p.

2 Addition and subtraction
Examples on addition and subtraction using items from the Goodies catalogue could be given, for example:
Find the total cost of
(a) a football and a rugby ball,
(b) a pair of ice skates and a table tennis set.
Find the difference in cost between
(a) a badminton set and twistball,
(b) a bicycle helmet and a lighting set.

Additional activity

How many can you buy?
Q8 could be extended by asking pupils to find the maximum/minimum number of items which can be purchased for a total of £100, given that only one of any particular item or size of item can be bought.

Q10 could be extended to find the maximum number of items which can be purchased over 20 weeks for a total weekly payment of up to £4·50.

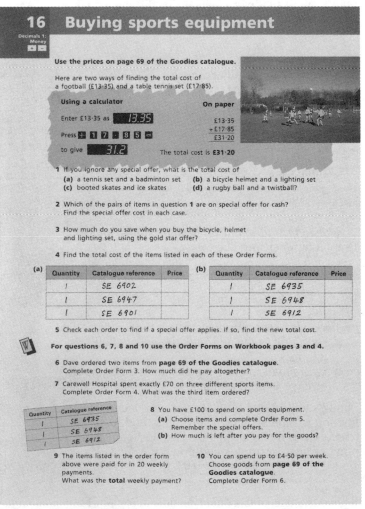

16 Buying sports equipment

Decimals 1:
Money

Use the prices on page 69 of the Goodies catalogue.

Here are two ways of finding the total cost of a football (£13·35) and a table tennis set (£17·85).

Using a calculator   **On paper**

Enter £13·35 as **13.35**   £13·35
                                                                            +£17·85
Press **+ 1 7 . 8 5 =**   £31·20

to give **31.2**   The total cost is **£31·20**

1 If you ignore any special offer, what is the total cost of
   (a) a tennis set and a badminton set   (b) a bicycle helmet and a lighting set
   (c) booted skates and ice skates   (d) a rugby ball and a twistball?

2 Which of the pairs of items in question 1 are on special offer for cash? Find the special offer cost in each case.

3 How much do you save when you buy the bicycle, helmet and lighting set, using the gold star offer?

4 Find the total cost of the items listed in each of these Order Forms.

(a)
Quantity	Catalogue reference	Price
1	SE 6902	
1	SE 6947	
1	SE 6901	

(b)
Quantity	Catalogue reference	Price
1	SE 6935	
1	SE 6948	
1	SE 6912	

5 Check each order to find if a special offer applies. If so, find the new total cost.

For questions 6, 7, 8 and 10 use the Order Forms on Workbook pages 3 and 4.

6 Dave ordered two items from **page 69 of the Goodies catalogue.** Complete Order Form 3. How much did he pay altogether?

7 Carewell Hospital spent exactly £70 on three different sports items. Complete Order Form 4. What was the third item ordered?

Quantity	Catalogue reference
1	SE 6935
1	SE 6948
1	SE 6912

8 You have £100 to spend on sports equipment.
   (a) Choose items and complete Order Form 5. Remember the special offers.
   (b) How much is left after you pay for the goods?

9 The items listed in the order form above were paid for in 20 weekly payments. What was the **total** weekly payment?

10 You can spend up to £4·50 per week. Choose goods from **page 69 of the Goodies catalogue.** Complete Order Form 6.

Equipment

Calculator.

Content

- Multiplication of one- and two-place decimals by 2 to 10, and 100
- Addition and subtraction of two-place decimals.

Organisation

The Introductory activity should precede Q7.

Introductory activity

Multiplication by 10, 100
The rules for multiplying one- and two-place decimals by 10 and 100 should be revised, for example:
Lollipops cost 8p or £0·08 each so:

(a) 10 cost
$10 \times 8p = 80p$ *or* $10 \times £0·08 = £0·80$
The digits move 1 place left.

(b) 100 cost
$100 \times 8p = 800p$ *or* $100 \times £0·08 = £8·00$
The digits move 2 places left.

Possible further examples are:
Find the cost of 10 and 100 of each item:

(a) bars of chocolate at £0·23 each
(b) packets of sweets at £1·24 each
(c) bags of toffees at £2·07 each
(d) boxes of chocolates at £11·50 each.

A reel has 2·4 metres of thread. What length of thread is in (a) 10 reels, (b) 100 reels?

Detailed notes

Q3 The total cost of all three is required.

Q4 The rate of pay is 346·5p per hour. Whilst the half-pence is no longer a coin of currency fractions of a pence are frequently used in everyday life. Accept answers in pounds or pence.

Q6 Some pupils may not interpret 3 pairs as 6 curtains.

Equipment

None.

Content

- Interpretation of information in written or diagrammatic form
- Calculator multiplication of one- and two-place decimals by one-, two- and three-digit whole numbers
- Addition and subtraction of one- and two-place decimals.

Organisation

See page 3 of these notes for information on the use of the Goodies catalogue.

Introductory activity 1 should be carried out before pupils do Q1 to Q4. Introductory activity 2 should then take place before pupils complete the work on the page.

Introductory activities

1 Calculator multiplication
Discuss with the pupils how to perform a multiplication using a calculator. A method is indicated in the panel. Completing examples like those in Q1 should help to ensure that each pupil masters the techniques involved.

2 Hire-purchase
Q5 to Q7 ask for a comparison between the cost of paying for the goods over 20 weeks and the cash price. Discuss the advantages and disadvantages of this system of payment. Explain that it usually costs more to use this method of purchase, sometimes considerably so. However sometimes it works out to be the same as the cash price but it is unlikely to be less.

Discuss the example illustrated in the panel.

Detailed notes

Q3 This use of average may have to be explained. Some pupils may need reminding that there are 52 weeks in a year.

Q4a Information from Q3 is needed.

Q7 Some pupils may misinterpret this question by thinking that Ali has made 3 weekly payments when he has actually made 22.

Equipment

Calculator.

18
Decimals 1:
Multiplication
using a
calculator

N3e/4

PSE
RTN/D4
MD/D4

Content

- Interpretation and completion of diagrams
- Concept of a tenth, first decimal place as a fraction.

Introductory activity

See Introductory activity 1 for Core Textbook page 14. This activity could be repeated for different shapes. For example:

Make shapes or show drawings where the tenths are shaded, say 6 tenths red, 4 tenths blue. Ask what fraction is

(a) red, (b) blue,
(c) coloured.

It is important that pupils realise that the red and blue together make ten tenths or one whole.

Detailed notes

Q1 Help may be required in interpreting the table.
Q2 Decimal fractions are expected.
Q3 Any three colours may be used.
Q4 Three forms of recording are required.

Additional activity

Coloured strips
Ask pupils to make coloured strips to represent different fractions or mixed numbers. For example: 7 tenths, 1·3, $2\frac{3}{10}$.

Equipment

Coloured pencils.

S8
Decimals 1:
First decimal
place +,−

N2a, 3c/
3 → 4
SM4b/
3 → 4

RTN/D3
AS/D

Content

- Interpretation and completion of scales marked in tenths
- Ordering of one-place decimals
- Addition and subtraction of one-place decimals in weight.

Organisation

Introductory activities 1 and 2 should be carried out before pupils attempt Q1 to Q3. Introductory activity 3 should then take place before pupils complete the work on the page.

Introductory activities

1 Revision of tenths using a number line
See Introductory activity 2 for Core Textbook page 14.

2 Revision of tenths using scales
Many scales, including those found on rulers, tape measures, bathroom scales, kitchen scales, thermometers and so on, are marked in tenths. Any practical work which involves the use of these scales would be beneficial.

3 Addition and subtraction
The language and recording recommended for addition and subtraction is described on page T2 of these notes. It may help motivate pupils if examples made use of practical data gathered by the pupils, for example, measuring lengths and then finding the sum and the difference. Possible initial graded examples could be,
Addition:

(a) 3·6 + 2·1, 5·4 + 3·5
(b) 3·6 + 2·7, 5·4 + 3·6
(c) 3·6 + 9·7, 5·4 + 4·6

Subtraction:

(a) 5·6 − 3·4, 8·7 − 5·2
(b) 6·3 − 2·5, 7·1 − 6·8

Detailed notes

Q5 Help in interpreting the table may be required. Answers should be recorded as in Q4.

Equipment

For Introductory activities 2 and 3 measuring equipment such as metre tapes and weighing scales which are marked in tenths.

Content

- Interpretation and completion of diagrams
- Concept of a hundredth, second decimal place as a fraction.

Introductory activity

See Introductory activity 1 for Core Textbook page 15.

Detailed notes

Q2 Any 'pattern' of shading is acceptable.

Equipment

Coloured pencil.

Content

- Interpretation of tabular information
- Addition and subtraction of two-place decimals in money
- Problem solving: listing.

Introductory activity

The language and recording recommended for addition and subtraction is described on page T2 of these notes.

Menu prices
The information on this menu could be used for initial addition and subtraction calculations. For example:

```
Farren's Fish Shop: Menu
Pizza & chips      £2·46
Fish & chips       £2·50
Chicken & chips    £2·75
```

Find the total cost of:
(a) Pizza & chips and Fish & chips
(b) Fish & chips and Chicken & chips

Find the difference in cost between:
(a) Chicken & chips and Fish & chips
(b) Chicken & chips and Pizza & chips

Detailed notes

Menu   The words 'Starters', 'Main', 'Sweets' may need explanation.

Q4   Combinations should include: starters + main, main + sweet, starters + sweet.

Equipment

None.

S10
Decimals 1:
Second
decimal place
+,−

N3c, 4b/4

PSE
RTN/D4
AS/D2

Content

- Interpretation of diagrams
- Multiplication of one- and two-place decimals by 2 to 9 in volume, weight and money
- Addition of two-place decimals in money.

Introductory activity

Multiplying prices
Possible initial examples on multiplication are:

'Babysoft' soap powder is sold in packets containing 2·8 kg. What weight is in
(a) 3, (b) 7, (c) 8 packets?

A soft toy costs £1·84. Find the cost of
(a) 4, (b) 5, (c) 9 soft toys.

Equipment

None.

S11
Decimals 1:
Multiplication
by 2 to 9

N3c, 4ab/
4 → 5

RTN/D4
AS/D2
MD/D3

Content

- Interpretation of information in written, tabular and diagrammatic form
- Calculator multiplication of one- and two-place decimals by two-digit whole numbers in volume, weight and money
- Subtraction of two-place decimals in money.

Introductory activity

See Introductory activity 1 for Core Textbook page 18.

Detailed notes

Q1   Help may be needed in interpreting the table.

Q3 to 5   The information needed is available in Q1 and Q2.

Q5   The term 'profit' may need to be explained.

Equipment

Calculator.

S12
Decimals 1:
× using a
calculator

N3ce/3;
4b/4

RTN/D3,
D4
AS/D3
MD/D4

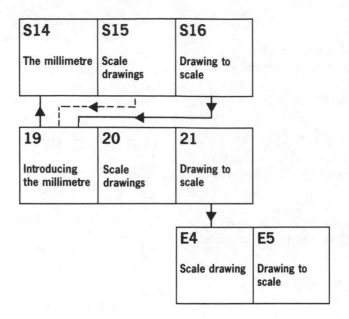

CONTENT AND DEVELOPMENT

Core

Previous measure work should have covered drawing and measuring to the nearest half centimetre, simple scale calculations and drawing lengths to scale.

In *Length and scale*, this work is consolidated and developed to cover:

- introduction of the millimetre and its relationship with the centimetre
- measurement to the nearest millimetre
- calculation of scaled lengths and true lengths using given scales
- construction of scale drawings.

Support

S14 to S16 may be used either as lead-in material or as an alternative to the work in the Core Textbook.

S14 supports the work of Core Textbook page 19.
S15 supports the work of Core Textbook page 20.
S16 supports the work of Core Textbook page 21.

Extension

This material extends the work on scale calculations and includes construction of a 3D model from a 2D representation.

National Curriculum (England and Wales)

UA2bd, 3c
SM2b, 3d, 4ab

Mathematics 5–14 (Scotland)

PSE
RTN/D4
RN/D1
ME/D1, E1
PFS/E3
RS/D1, E4

RELATED ACTIVITIES

Uses of scale
Pupils could bring in examples of scales used in everyday life, for example, models, maps and house plans.

EQUIPMENT

Ruler marked in cm and mm, ruler marked in $\frac{1}{2}$ cm, metre sticks or tapes, calculator, 1 cm squared paper, pipecleaners or string, sticky tape.
For the Introductory activities: cardboard scales or scales drawn onto an overhead projector slide, sketches of various objects, for example, trees, ships, etc., model car.

Content

- Introduction to the millimetre (mm) and measurement to the nearest millimetre
- Centimetre/millimetre relationship
- Approximation to the nearest centimetre.

Introductory activity

Using millimetre rulers

Large scales (to represent rulers) of the type shown at the top of Core Textbook page 19 could be prepared on cardboard or an overhead projector (OHP) slide and used to illustrate the different markings which may appear on rulers. Lines of the same length, drawn on the blackboard or OHP could be measured by the different rulers in turn and the different ways of recording discussed.

The numbers represent centimetres.
The length is between 4 cm and 5 cm.

The numbers represent millimetres.
The length is about 43 mm.

Each small interval is 1 millimetre.
The length is about 4 cm 3 mm.

Some oral practice in changing from millimetres to centimetres and *vice versa* would be worthwhile.

Detailed notes

| Panel above Q1 | The relationship and forms of recording used in the panel must be understood before attempting Q4. |

| Q4c | The lengths from part (a) should be changed to mm and a calculator used to find the average. Inaccurate measurement can lead to a calculator answer which has to be rounded to the nearest whole number. |

Equipment

Ruler marked in cm and mm, calculator.
For the Introductory activity: cardboard scales or scales drawn onto an OHP.

Content

- Measurement to the nearest millimetre
- Interpretation of scale drawings using simple scales
- Centimetre/millimetre relationship.

The ratio form, for example, 1:50 is not used until Heinemann Mathematics 8.

Introductory activity

Calculation of true lengths

Sketches of various objects, for example, trees, ships, etc. could be prepared using scales such as 1 cm to 4 cm or 1 cm to 5 m. Discussion should centre around how to calculate true lengths, widths, heights, etc:

- Measure the length on the sketch, the scaled length, say 12·4 cm.
- Read the scale, say 1 cm to 3 m.
- Calculate the true length:
  1 cm represents 3 m
  12·4 cm represents $3 \times 12\cdot4 = 37\cdot2$ m.

$$\begin{array}{r} 12\cdot4 \\ \times 3 \\ \hline 37\cdot2 \end{array}$$

The method of calculation may be mental or written depending on its complexity.

Detailed notes

| Q2 | A calculator may be used for the Golden Eagle calculation. |

Additional activity

True lengths

The true lengths found by calculations on this page could be discussed in relation to the pupils' surroundings. For example, the Malaysian butterfly has a wingspan as wide as the textbook page; the albatross's wingspan may be more than half the classroom width; the Shuttle's wingspan, at around 30 metres, may be three times the length of the classroom, and so on.

Equipment

Ruler marked in cm and mm, a calculator may be required by some pupils.
For the Introductory activity: sketches of various objects, for example, trees, ships, etc.

21

Length and
scale:
Drawing to
scale

UA2bd,
3c/5
SM3d/6

PSE
ME/E1
PFS/E3

Content

- Interpretation of diagrams
- Calculation of scaled lengths given true lengths and simple scales
- Construction of scale drawings from rough sketches
- Working systematically, use of trial and improvement strategy.

Introductory activity

Calculation of scaled lengths

Ask the pupils how they would make a map or plan of part of the school, for example, the hall, playground or a classroom. Discussion should highlight the need to

- make a *rough sketch*
- measure the *true lengths*
- choose an appropriate *scale*
- calculate the *scaled lengths*
- make an accurate *scale drawing*.

When calculating scaled lengths the pupils should be clear about how a scale such as 1 cm to 4 m can be used 'in reverse':

4 m is represented by 1 cm

If a wall of length 12 m is to be shown using this scale then a division is needed to find how many lengths are contained in a 12 m length.

4 m is represented by 1 cm
12 m is represented by $12 \div 4 = 3$ cm

Equipment

Ruler marked in cm and mm, 1 cm squared paper.

Detailed notes

Q1 The three scale drawings should be compared to show how the final size reflects the choice of scale.

Q2 Some of the scaled lengths involve half centimetres.

Q3 A trial and improvement strategy is likely.

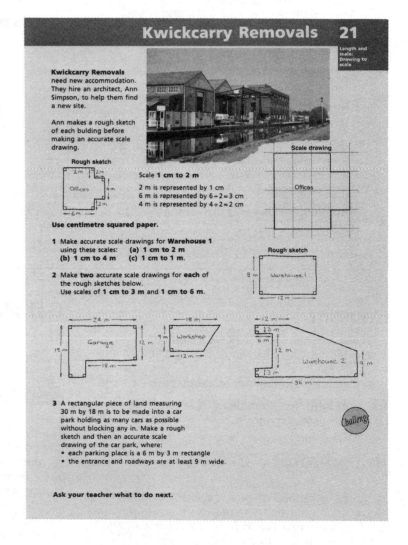

S14
Length and scale:
The millimetre

SM4b/4;
4a/5

RTN/D4
ME/D1

Content

■ Measurement to the nearest millimetre
■ Centimetre/millimetre relationship.

Introductory activity

The Introductory activity for Core Textbook page 19 can be used.

Additional activity

Worm lines
Pupils could be asked to draw some worms of their own. This may be done in two ways:
■ Measurements could be given and pupils would draw worms of this given length. The lengths could be given in the various forms such as 36 mm, 3 cm 6 mm or 3·6 cm.
■ Pupils could draw their own worms and have the worms measured and recorded by a partner. The lengths could be entered in a table similar to the one used in Q2.

Equipment

Ruler marked in cm and mm.

S15
Length and scale:
Scale drawings

SM3d/
5 → 6

ME/D1
PFS/E3

Content

■ Measurement of lines to the nearest half centimetre
■ Calculation of true length using simple scales.

Introductory activity

Models
Show pupils a model of a car or train and discuss how the size of a scale model is decided.
Discussion should bring out the following points:
■ all true lengths are reduced by the same factor
■ different scales will make different sized models.

The sketch below could then be reproduced on a blackboard or OHP and used to find the *true* sizes of the measurements indicated.

Scale: 1 cm to 2 m

2·5 cm

5 cm

The true length is 5 × 2 = 10 m
The true height is 2·5 × 2 = 5 m

The units used in the true lengths should be highlighted.

Detailed notes

Q2 You may wish to discuss the scales used showing that although the objects are drawn the same height on the page, their true heights are different.

Equipment

Ruler marked in cm and mm.
For the Introductory activity: model car.

S16
Length and
scale:
Drawing to
scale

**SM3d/
5 → 6**

**ME/D1, E1
PFS/E3**

Content

- Calculation of scaled length given true length and simple scales
- Drawing straight lines accurately to the nearest millimetre to represent scaled lengths
- Centimetre/millimetre relationship in the form 3·6 cm is 36 mm.

Introductory activity

Calculation of scaled lengths
Before pupils attempt the work of the page they should measure the length of the classroom to the nearest metre. Ask the pupils how they would go about drawing a straight line to represent, for example, the length of the classroom. Discussion should highlight the need to:
- measure the *true length*
- choose an appropriate *scale*
- calculate the *scaled length*
- draw the line *accurately* using a ruler.

Discussion of a method for calculating the scaled lengths is likely to be necessary, see the Introductory activity suggested for Core Textbook page 21.

Equipment

Ruler marked in cm and mm, 2 metre sticks, a calculator may be necessary.

Detailed notes

Q2 Calculation of the scaled length should be done mentally

Q3 The 'awkward' calculation is the worked example. Nevertheless some pupils may require to use a calculator for the other examples.

Q4a Some pupils may need to measure their own height.

Q4b The sketches are not expected to be drawn to scale.

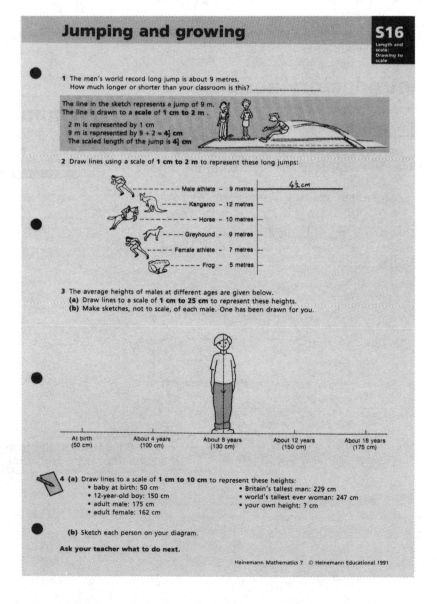

Jumping and growing

S16
Length and
scale:
Drawing to
scale

1 The men's world record long jump is about 9 metres.
How much longer or shorter than your classroom is this? _____

The line in the sketch represents a jump of 9 m.
The line is drawn to a **scale** of **1 cm to 2 m**.

2 m is represented by 1 cm
9 m is represented by 9 ÷ 2 = 4½ cm
The scaled length of the jump is 4½ cm

2 Draw lines using a scale of **1 cm to 2 m** to represent these long jumps:

Male athlete – 9 metres   4½ cm
Kangaroo – 12 metres
Horse – 10 metres
Greyhound – 9 metres
Female athlete – 7 metres
Frog – 5 metres

3 The average heights of males at different ages are given below.
(a) Draw lines to a scale of **1 cm to 25 cm** to represent these heights.
(b) Make sketches, not to scale, of each male. One has been drawn for you.

At birth   About 4 years   About 8 years   About 12 years   About 18 years
(50 cm)   (100 cm)   (130 cm)   (150 cm)   (175 cm)

4 (a) Draw lines to a scale of **1 cm to 10 cm** to represent these heights:
- baby at birth: 50 cm
- 12-year-old boy: 150 cm
- adult male: 175 cm
- adult female: 162 cm
- Britain's tallest man: 229 cm
- world's tallest ever woman: 247 cm
- your own height: ? cm

(b) Sketch each person on your diagram.

Ask your teacher what to do next.

Heinemann Mathematics 7 © Heinemann Educational 1991

Content

- Calculation of true length given scaled length and scale
- Measurement to the nearest millimetre.

Detailed notes

Q3 Two blocks of wood can help in measuring the length of a model.

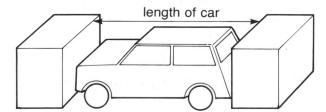

length of car

E4
Length and scale: Scale drawings

SM3d/
5 → 6

RTN/D4
ME/E1
PFS/E3

Q5 A pipecleaner could be bent to match each curve and the distance marked. The pipecleaner is then straightened and the marked length measured with a ruler. String could also be used to find the curved distances.

Equipment

Calculator, pipecleaner or string.

Content

- Calculation of scaled length given true length and scale
- Construction of a 3D model
- Interpretation of information presented in visual form.

Organisation

Q2 requires pupils to work in pairs.

Detailed notes

Panel above Q1 Some pupils may realise that the scale 1 cm to 50 cm is the same as 1 cm to 0·5 m and calculate scaled lengths in this way:

0·5 m is represented by 1 cm
1·0 m is represented by 2 cm

Q2a Pupils should check that their drawings of the gable ends and walls are the same size.

E5
Length and scale: Drawing to scale

SM2b/4;
3d/5 → 6

ME/D1
RS/D1, E4
PFS/E3

Q2b The cottage will be more rigid if the whole roof is constructed from a single piece of card rather than from two pieces. Some pupils might overhang the roof as it would be in reality.

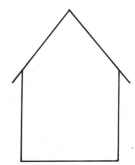

Q2c Tape should be used to stick the pieces together. It is recommended that the tape is used inside the construction where it is hidden from view as far as is possible.

Equipment

Ruler, calculator, sticky tape.

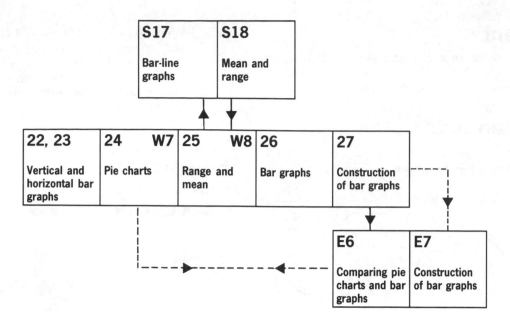

CONTENT AND DEVELOPMENT

Core

Previously pupils should have carried out work involving the organisation of data in a frequency table, the interpretation of bar, bar-line and straight-line graphs including some construction of simple examples of these graphs.

In *Handling data 1*, this work is consolidated and developed to cover:

- using discrete data, interpretation and construction of vertical and horizontal bar and combined bar graphs
- interpretation and construction of pie charts subdivided into 5, 10 and 24 parts
- calculation of range and mean
- collection and organisation of measurement data and its display as a bar graph.

Handling data 2 deals with the interpretation and construction of line graphs in 'trend' and 'conversion' graph forms (see pages 65–70 of these notes).

Handling data 3 deals with the use of frequency tables and frequency diagrams with class intervals (see pages 135–138 of these notes).

Support

The work on S17 and S18 is linked with Core Textbook page 25 and W8. It can be used as lead-in work to the Core or as support work for those pupils who have found the Core difficult.

The ideas in the Core are reinforced through the interpretation and construction of simple horizontal and vertical bar-line graphs.

Extension

E6 and E7 may be used following successful completion of Core Textbook pages. However, since E6 contains new ideas about pie charts it could be attempted immediately after Core Textbook page 24 and W7. After returning to and completing the Core, E7 could then be attempted.

The new ideas on E6 are

- pie charts subdivided into 100 equal parts representing percentage
- comparison of the effectiveness of pie and bar charts when displaying the *same* data.

National Curriculum (England and Wales)

N3d
HD2abcdefg

Mathematics 5–14 (Scotland)

PSE C/C1, C2, D1, E1
O/C1, D1   D/C2, D1
I/C2, D1, E1, E3   MD/D4

RELATED ACTIVITIES

Where are graphs useful?
Graphs are used in many other areas of the curriculum such as science, geography, etc. When introducing the new ideas of this section data could be taken from these cross-curricular sources thus reinforcing the widespread importance of this area of mathematics.

Encourage pupils to collect a wide variety of types of graphs by cutting them from newspapers, magazines, etc. These can be mounted for wall display and discussed.

EQUIPMENT

2 mm, $\frac{1}{2}$ cm and 1 cm squared paper, 150 cm tape, two dice, newspapers (each containing the results of 25 football matches), calculator, coloured pencils.

Content

- Introduction of vertical and horizontal bar and combined bar graphs
- Collection and organisation of data and its presentation as bar and combined bar graphs
- Calculation of average.

Introductory activity

Different forms of bar graph
The information below, about the number of pupils in a class having preference for particular colours of car, could be displayed.

> 6 pupils preferred red
> 5 pupils preferred yellow
> 9 pupils preferred blue

Draw two bar graphs using this data side by side as shown. Coloured chalk could be helpful.

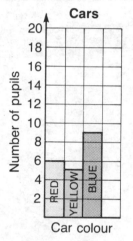
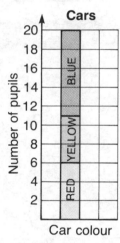

Question the pupils about the graphs: 'Which colour was preferred by the greatest/smallest number of pupils?' 'How many pupils altogether preferred red, yellow or blue cars?'

Discussion should emphasise that
- the side-by-side arrangement is best for *comparison*
- the end-on-end arrangement is best for *finding totals*.

A horizontal presentation of the graphs could also be discussed.

HD2cf/3;
2ab/4;
2d/5

C/D1
O/D1
D/D
I/D1, E3

Detailed notes

22,Q1 23,Q1 It may be necessary to clarify what is meant by the different categories of holiday places and the context of vehicle ferries.

22,Q4,5 23,Q3,4 These questions are expected to be answered through visual inspection.

22,Q6 23,Q6 Guidance may be required by some pupils concerning some of the following: collection of data, classification of holiday places/vehicles, choice of squared paper, choice of scale, colour key, lay-out of combined bars and spaces.

Equipment

$\frac{1}{2}$ cm or 1 cm squared paper, coloured pencils.

N3d/4
HD2c/
4 → 6;
2f/5

C/D1
O/D1
D/D1
I/D1

Content

- Interpretation of pie charts subdivided into 5, 10 and 24 parts
- Construction of pie charts subdivided into 10 and 24 parts.

Introductory activity

Pie charts

This new form of graph could be introduced through discussion in turn of appropriate diagrams:

How we come to school

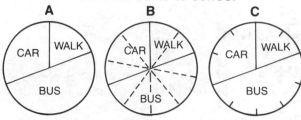

A   B   C

For **A** pupils should answer questions using visual inspection:

'How do most/fewest pupils come to school?'
'What fraction of all the pupils come by bus?'
'Do more or less than one quarter of the pupils come by car?'

Now suppose the graph represents ten pupils. Feint or dotted lines could be drawn to divide the circle into ten equal sections as in **B**.
Each sector or part of the circle represents one pupil.

'How many of these pupils come by bus?'
'How many walk to school?'

Explain that the feint or dotted lines may not be shown and that the circumference can be marked as in **C**.

Equipment

Coloured pencils.

Detailed notes

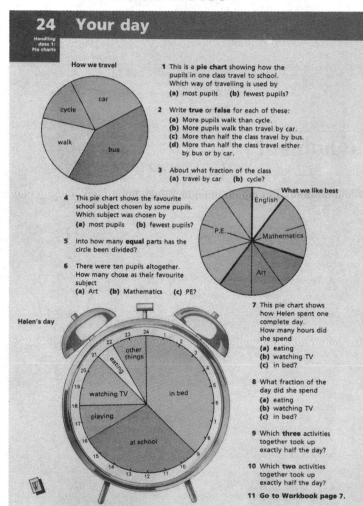

24   Your day

Handling data 1: Pie charts

How we travel

1 This is a **pie chart** showing how the pupils in one class travel to school. Which way of travelling is used by
(a) most pupils   (b) fewest pupils?

2 Write **true** or **false** for each of these:
(a) More pupils walk than cycle.
(b) More pupils walk than travel by car.
(c) More than half the class travel by bus.
(d) More than half the class travel either by bus or by car.

3 About what fraction of the class
(a) travel by car   (b) cycle?

What we like best

4 This pie chart shows the favourite school subject chosen by some pupils. Which subject was chosen by
(a) most pupils   (b) fewest pupils?

5 Into how many **equal** parts has the circle been divided?

6 There were ten pupils altogether. How many chose as their favourite subject
(a) Art   (b) Mathematics   (c) PE?

Helen's day

7 This pie chart shows how Helen spent one complete day. How many hours did she spend
(a) eating
(b) watching TV
(c) in bed?

8 What fraction of the day did she spend
(a) eating
(b) watching TV
(c) in bed?

9 Which **three** activities together took up exactly half the day?

10 Which **two** activities together took up exactly half the day?

11 Go to Workbook page 7.

Q2 | The *true* or *false* form of answer may need to be stressed.

Q3 | Answers should be found by visual inspection and will be approximate.

Q6 | This can only be answered correctly if Q5 has been answered correctly.

Q7 | Discussion should highlight that the circumference of the circle has 24 equal parts each representing 1 hour. So the circle represents the whole 24-hour day.

Q9 | There are several acceptable answers here.

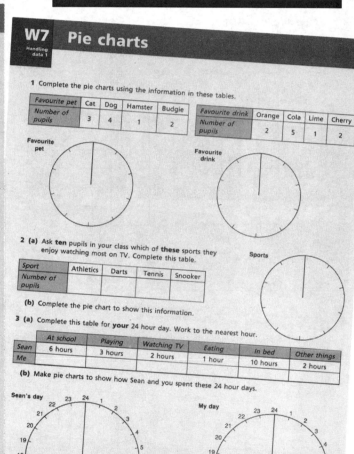

W7   Pie charts

Handling data 1

1 Complete the pie charts using the information in these tables.

Favourite pet	Cat	Dog	Hamster	Budgie
Number of pupils	3	4	1	2

Favourite drink	Orange	Cola	Lime	Cherry
Number of pupils	2	5	1	2

Favourite pet

Favourite drink

2 (a) Ask **ten** pupils in your class which of **these** sports they enjoy watching most on TV. Complete this table.

Sport	Athletics	Darts	Tennis	Snooker
Number of pupils				

Sports

(b) Complete the pie chart to show this information.

3 (a) Complete this table for **your** 24 hour day. Work to the nearest hour.

	At school	Playing	Watching TV	Eating	In bed	Other things
Sean	6 hours	3 hours	2 hours	1 hour	10 hours	2 hours
Me						

(b) Make pie charts to show how Sean and you spent these 24 hour days.

Sean's day

My day

Go to Textbook page 25.

W7,Q2 | The information which is collected could be recorded by inserting tally marks in the table.

W7,Q3 | This should be a typical school day with times rounded *to the nearest hour*. The 'other things' category ensures a 24-hour total for the day.

25
W8
Handling
data 1:
Range and
mean

HD2c/4;
2de/5

O/C1
D/C2
I/D1, E1, E3

Content

- Interpretation of information from a table
- Calculation of range and mean
- Organisation of data in a frequency table and display as a bar graph.

The concept of range is developed further when data is grouped using class intervals (see Core Textbook pages 107 to 109).

Introductory activity

Revision of calculation of range and mean
Using suitable sets of discrete data remind the pupils how to find the range and calculate the mean. For example, using points scored in a 'Hoopla' game:

Alan has five throws and scores 5, 5, 6, 6, 8.

    Range (8 − 5) = 3   Mean score 30 ÷ 5 = 6

Jack has seven throws and scores 3, 4, 5, 5, 5, 6, 7.

    Range (7 − 3) = 4   Mean score 35 ÷ 7 = 5

The example also shows how the mean can be used to make a comparison of performance even if the numbers of items of data are not equal.

Detailed notes

Q5 Encourage the pupils to add *mentally* from left to right (holes 1 to 18) then check by adding from right to left (holes 18 to 1).

Q6 Discuss how the mean may be used to compare performance. This can also be done by noting the *total* scores since on this occasion each player has 18 scores.

Q7 Discuss the need to read each row of scores carefully so that none is omitted. Encourage the pupils to check that the *total* of the Frequency column is 18.

Additional activity

Bar graph shapes
Discuss the pupils' results for W8. For example, although Rashmi and Dean have the same mean score of 3 the distribution of scores and the consequent shape of graph are quite different.

Equipment

Calculator.

26
Handling
data 1:
Bar graphs

HD2c/4

C/C2
O/C1
D/C2
I/D1

Content

- Interpretation and construction of frequency tables and bar graphs
- Collection and organisation of measurement data and its display as a bar graph.

These graphs should show the normal 'bunching' near a central value and a 'tailing off' at the extremes.

Introductory activity

Measuring to the nearest centimetre
A brief discussion with pupils of taking measurements and rounding them *to the nearest centimetre* should be followed by some practical measurement, for example, of neck, ankle, headband, etc.

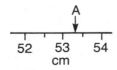

A is between 53 cm and 54 cm.
A is nearer to 53 cm.
A is *53 cm to the nearest cm.*

Detailed notes

Q2 This kind of information is of special interest to manufacturers and stockists of footwear.

Q5 $\frac{1}{2}$ cm or 1 cm squared paper would be suitable.

Q6 This can be answered from the table. However encourage pupils to use their graph. Additional questions corresponding to those in Q3 could be asked.

Q7 'Year group' is used to imply more than one class. About 50 to 60 pupils would be appropriate. Understanding could be consolidated by asking questions about the pupils' graphs similar to those in Q6.

Equipment

150 cm tape, $\frac{1}{2}$ cm or 1 cm squared paper.

27

Handling
data 1:
Construction
of bar graphs

HD2c/4

C/E1
O/C1
D/C1
I/C2

Content

- Collection and organisation of 'real-life' data
- Display of this data as a bar graph.

These graphs should show the distribution of data collected as 'skewed'.

Detailed notes

Q1 Discuss this question and ask for suggestions of how the collection of data could be organised. For example:

- working in pairs – one pupil throws the dice 50 times while the other enters tally marks in the table. They then change roles.

2	0	1	1						
		and so on							

- working in a group – pupils take turns to throw the dice while one pupil enters the differences in a 100 square as shown. The completed square is used by all the pupils to enter tally marks in their tables.

Q1c It is hoped that pupils will now be able to

- choose a suitable size of squared paper
- choose a scale for the frequency axis to ensure the graph is of a reasonable size and thus easy to interpret
- position and label each axis suitably
- give the graph a title.

Q1d In theory the difference of 1 should occur most frequently with 2 next.

Q2 Discussion may be needed about how to organise the collection of the data in pairs. It is desirable to have a number of newspapers with results for different weeks.

Q2d The most likely score is 1 goal. Even when the results for different sets of matches are used the graphs are likely to be similar.

Equipment

Two dice, newspapers each showing the results of at least 25 football matches, 2 mm, $\frac{1}{2}$ cm and 1 cm squared paper (pupils to *select* from these).

S17

Handling
data 1:
Bar-line
graphs

HD2cf/4

D/C2
I/C2

Content

- Interpretation and construction of horizontal bar-line graphs.

Introductory activity

From bar graph to bar-line graph

Construct a bar graph with the pupils, for example, based on the times taken by six pupils to travel to school. Focus on

- the organisation of the data in a frequency table
- the minimum and maximum times taken leading to the selection of a suitable scale on the Time axis
- the positioning of the numbers on the Time axis
- the positioning of the pupils' names on the Name axis.

Follow up the construction of the bar graph with a discussion about the width of the bars being

unimportant. Changing the width does not change the information conveyed. Suggest that instead of a 'bar', a line or a spike could be used. Emphasise that this could have implications for the positioning of the pupils' names since it is easier to draw the spike on top of a grid line.

Detailed notes

Q1 Pupils may need to discuss the names of the Greek island resorts.

Q2 Pupils should realise that part of the map has been enlarged.

Q3 Squared paper should be used to construct the bar-line graph. The format used in Q1 and Q2 is suitable.

Equipment

$\frac{1}{2}$ cm or 1 cm squared paper.

S18

Handling
data 1:
Mean and
range

HD2f/4;
2d/5

O/C1
I/C2
MD/D4

Content

- Interpretation of information presented in a table
- Organisation of data in a frequency table and display as a vertical bar-line graph
- Calculation of range and mean.

Introductory activity

Train journey costs

Draw a bar-line graph for some costs, for example, the cost of a journey by train. Use real or simulated data for 4 adults (£8 each), 6 children (£4 each) and 2 pets (£2 each). Focus on

- the organisation of the data in a frequency table

- the range of prices involved
- use of the range of prices to determine suitable labelling on the Cost axis to construct a bar-line graph
- the mean cost of the journey (£5).

Detailed notes

Q1d Pupils may like to tick or score out each cost as a tally mark is recorded.

Q2 Pupils may need to discuss that drachmas are Greek currency.

Equipment

Calculator.

Content

- Interpretation of pie charts
- Construction of bar graphs using information from pie charts
- Comparison of pie charts and bar graphs.

Detailed notes

Q5 Initial help may be required. For example, by building up a rough sketch, as shown below, to highlight the need to choose
- suitable labels for each axis
- a suitable scale for the '% heat loss' axis.

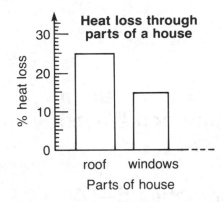

Q5,7 Pupils should use the same colours for each matching 'bar' and pie chart sector.

Q6 On completion of this question discuss the relative merits of bar graph and pie chart presentation of the same information. Pupils should realise
- the pie chart is better for showing fractional parts of the complete set of data
- the bar graph is better for reading actual values and differences in the data.

Additional activity

Pie charts in newspapers
Bar graphs could be drawn from information presented in pie chart form in newspapers, magazines, etc. in order to find out if any information can be extracted more readily in the bar graph form.

Equipment

2 mm or ½ cm squared paper, coloured pencils.

Content

- Interpretation of information presented in visual form
- Collection and organisation of discrete data to form a frequency table
- Construction and comparison of bar graphs.

Detailed notes

Q2 It may be helpful to discuss with pupils that *they* have to
- choose a suitable size of squared paper
- choose a scale for the frequency axis to ensure the graph is of a reasonable size and thus easy to interpret
- position and label each axis suitably
- give the graph a title.

Q3,4 Answers can be found from either the frequency table or the graph.

Q6 Both graphs show that the most common score is 3. Their shapes are similar but the graph for holes 10 to 18 shows fewer higher scores (4s and 5s) and more lower scores (2s). Reasons for this could be discussed such as 'their skill improved as the game progressed' or 'holes 10 to 18 are easier/shorter than holes 1 to 9.'

Additional activities

1 Using scores for 18 holes
A frequency table could be constructed and a graph drawn using the scores for all 18 holes. This graph could then be compared with the other two.

2 Range and mean
The data could be used for further work on range and mean. For example:

- individual holes
  - hole 1, range (4–2) = 2
    mean 20 ÷ 6= 3·3 (approx.)
  - hole 4, range (4–1) = 3
    mean 15 ÷ 6 = 2·5
- sets of holes
  - holes 1–9, range (5–1), = 4
    mean 175 ÷ 54 = 3·24 (approx.)

Equipment

2 mm, ½ cm or 1 cm squared paper (pupils to *select* from these).

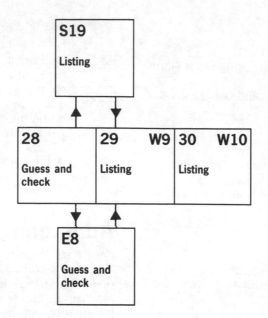

CONTENT AND DEVELOPMENT

Core

Previous work should have introduced pupils to solving mathematical problems and carrying out investigations. Many will have used strategies informally, including 'guess and check' and 'listing'.

In *Problem solving 1*, a more formal approach to using problem solving strategies is developed and covers:

- 'guess and, check and improve'
- 'listing'.

In *Problem solving 2* (on pages 112–115 of these notes), pupils are introduced to the strategy of 'look for a pattern'.

Support

S19 provides a lead-in to Core Textbook page 29.

Extension

E8 extends the work of Core Textbook page 28.

National Curriculum (England and Wales)

UA2ac

Mathematics 5–14 (Scotland)

PSE

EQUIPMENT

1 kg of beans, scales, set of dominoes, 1 cm and 2 cm squared paper, scissors, glue, calculator, coloured pencils.
For the Introductory activities: card of two different colours, clothes catalogue or magazine, red, blue, green and yellow counters.

28
Problem
solving 1:
Guess and
check

UA2a/4

PSE

Content

- Working methodically and recording findings systematically
- Selection of the mathematics needed
- Problem solving by a 'guess and check' strategy.

Organisation

Pupils could work in pairs so that questions are discussed. Part of problem solving for pupils is to interpret the question, so little help should be offered unless the pupils completely misinterpret what is asked.

Introductory activities

1 'Guess and check' in real life
Discuss real life situations which often demand the use of the 'guess and check' strategy. For example, finding the right key on a bunch of keys.

2 'Guess and check' to find the solution for a puzzle
Present the pupils with a simple puzzle, for example:

Place the numbers 1 to 9 in three circles so that the sum of the numbers in each circle is the same.

Encourage pupils to 'guess and check' each arrangement until a correct solution is found. Discuss how they worked to find the answer, for example, did they keep a record of each 'trial'? Some pupils might realise that if they add the numbers 1 to 9 and then divide by 3 they have the total for each circle. This makes it easier to arrange the numbers. Pupils should realise that 'guess and check' may take longer but a solution can usually be found, especially if a systematic approach to trials is adopted.

Detailed notes

Q2,3 The use of a calculator should allow pupils to concentrate on the *strategy* and avoid them being overwhelmed by the associated arithmetic.

Q4 Pupils are likely to weigh out a specific weight of beans, for example, 50 g, count the number in that weight, and *calculate* the approximate number in a kilogram. They should be aware that their answer is *approximate* and is likely to be different for another kilogram of beans.

Equipment

1 kg of beans, scales, 1 cm and 2 cm squared paper, scissors, glue, calculator.

Content

- Working methodically and recording findings systematically
- Problem solving by listing outcomes
  - using a letter code
  - in a table.

Organisation

Pupils may work in pairs to discuss the questions.

Introductory activities

1 Choosing outfits
When people buy a new item of clothing they often consider what it will go with in clothing they already own. Simulate this situation by using drawings or pictures from a clothes catalogue or magazine for items like these:

Pupils can be asked to choose one possible outfit, for example, a blue shirt, blue jeans and trainers with red trim. The outfit can be shown using the pictures or recorded as a sketch or in words. Further discussion should result in suggestions for other outfits. Each different outfit should be recorded until all eight possibilities have been identified.

2 Ways of systematic listing
Consider a shop selling two sizes of bags (large and small) in three different colours (red, green and blue).
Discuss ways of listing all the possible choices in an organised manner.
- using a letter code
- by completing a grid as on W9.

2 pairs of trainers
(1 pair with black trim,
1 pair with red trim)

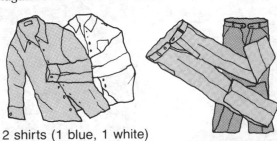

2 shirts (1 blue, 1 white)

2 pairs of jeans
(1 blue, 1 grey)

Equipment

$\frac{1}{2}$ and 1 cm squared paper.
For the Introductory activities: a clothes catalogue or magazine.

30
W10
Problem
solving 1:
Listing

UA2ac/4

PSE

Content

- Working methodically and recording findings systematically
- Problem solving by listing outcomes where
  – arrangement is ignored
  – arrangement is considered.

Organisation

Pupils should complete Introductory activity 1 before W10 and Introductory activity 2 before Core Textbook page 30.

Introductory activities

1 Combinations
W10 deals with combining items where the arrangement within the combination does not matter. Discuss this by considering examples like these:
Use 1 green, 1 red and 2 blue counters. Place the counters in pairs so that the two counters in each pair are of a different colour. Stress that the arrangement within each pair does not matter.

This can be repeated for other sets of counters, for example:

- 5 red, 2 blue and 3 green counters. Arrange the counters so that those in each pair are a different colour.

- 3 red, 3 blue and 2 green counters. Arrange the counters so that those in each pair are a different colour.

A variation requires counters, each a different colour, to be grouped in threes, for example:

- 3 red, 2 blue, 2 green and 2 yellow counters. Arrange the counters so that those in each three are a different colour.

2 Arrangements
Core Textbook page 30 deals with different arrangements of one set of items. Discuss the two different ways in which a red and a blue counter can be placed side by side.

Now, discuss the different ways in which three counters – red, blue and green – can be arranged

and so on.

Equipment

Coloured pencils.
For the Introductory activities: red, blue, green and yellow counters.

Detailed notes

W10,Q1 Pupils should mark in pencil the letters of the colours and only colour the drawings when they think they have solved the problem.

W10, Q2,3 A similar approach as in W10, Q1 is required when pairing and grouping in threes.

Q2 Remind the pupils that the arrangement or order in the group is important here.

Q6,7 Arrangements of four items are required.
Pupils are guided to a systematic approach by showing all the possible arrangements when the red light is in the first position.

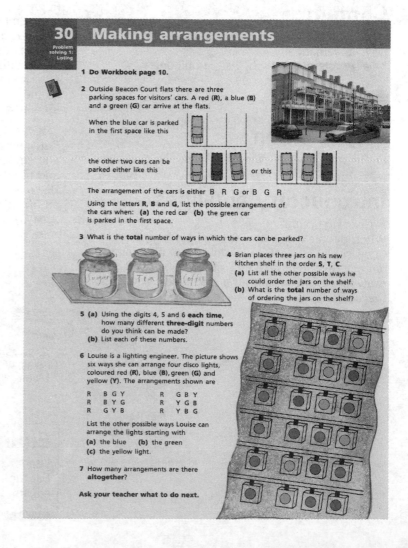

30 Making arrangements

1 Do Workbook page 10.

2 Outside Beacon Court flats there are three parking spaces for visitors' cars. A red (**R**), a blue (**B**) and a green (**G**) car arrive at the flats.

When the blue car is parked in the first space like this

the other two cars can be parked either like this   or this

The arrangement of the cars is either **B R G** or **B G R**

Using the letters **R**, **B** and **G**, list the possible arrangements of the cars when: (a) the red car (b) the green car is parked in the first space.

3 What is the **total** number of ways in which the cars can be parked?

4 Brian places three jars on his new kitchen shelf in the order **S, T, C**.
(a) List all the other possible ways he could order the jars on the shelf.
(b) What is the **total** number of ways of ordering the jars on the shelf?

5 (a) Using the digits 4, 5 and 6 **each time**, how many different **three-digit** numbers do you think can be made?
(b) List each of these numbers.

6 Louise is a lighting engineer. The picture shows six ways she can arrange four disco lights, coloured red (**R**), blue (**B**), green (**G**) and yellow (**Y**). The arrangements shown are

R B G Y   R G B Y
R B Y G   R Y G B
R G Y B   R Y B G

List the other possible ways Louise can arrange the lights starting with
(a) the blue   (b) the green
(c) the yellow light.

7 How many arrangements are there altogether?

Ask your teacher what to do next.

Content

- Interpretation of information presented in a table
- Selection of the mathematics required
- Working methodically and recording findings systematically
- Problem solving by listing outcomes in a table.

Introductory activity

Bus fares

Cut out rectangular pieces of card in two different colours to represent bus tickets at 40p for adults and 20p for children. Ask the pupils to work out the total bus fare for different groups such as 2 adults and 1 child. Build up a table showing 'Bus fares', like the one at the top of S19. When complete, ask the pupils to interpret the table, for example, the total fare for a group is £1·20, how many people *could* be in the group?

Detailed notes

Q1   Some discussion to facilitate interpretation of the table may be necessary.

Q1b   The form of recording is intended to prompt the pupils into considering a possible answer which is not shown in the table.

Q2a   Encourage systematic listing of totals on a row by row or column by column basis. Some pupils might spot the pattern and extend it.

Q2c   Three solutions will not be shown by the table (8 lollies and 1 ice, 10 lollies and 0 ices, 0 lollies and 5 ices).

Q3   Provision of centimetre squared paper should assist the presentation of data in a systematic manner.

Equipment

1 cm squared paper.
For the Introductory activity: card in two different colours.

S19
Problem solving 1: Listing

UA2ac/4

PSE

Content

- Working methodically and recording findings systematically
- Selection of the mathematics needed
- Problem solving by a 'guess and check' strategy.

Organisation

Pupils could work in pairs to discuss the questions.

Detailed notes

Q2   One possible method of recording is to write the numbers on either squared or plain paper and enclose each pair of numbers with a rectangle to represent a domino.

6	4	5	5
4	5	6	5
6	6	3	3
4	3	5	6

Q2a   Encourage a systematic approach to the 'guess and check', for example, here there is only one position in which two sixes are adjacent and so only one position for the | 6 | 6 | domino.

Similarly for the | 4 | 3 | domino.

Q2d   This has only one possible arrangement.

6	4	5	5
4	5	6	5
6	6	3	3
4	3	5	6

Equipment

Set of dominoes, 1 cm squared paper.

E8
Problem solving 1: Guess and check

UA2a/4

PSE

35

DETOURS IN PART 1

General advice about using the Detours can be found on page T6 of these notes.

9
W15
Detour:
Multiples and
factors

UA3c/4
N2a, 3a/4

MD/D1
PS/C1

Content

- The meaning of the terms multiple and factor.

Detailed notes

Q2,3,4 Suggest that the pupils try to find the factors using divisors systematically.

Q5 If necessary, explain that the factor pairs 3,4 and 4,3 are the same and count as a single pair. Pupils should realise that the right-hand diagram is the left-hand diagram rotated through 1 right angle.

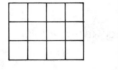

Equipment

Coloured pencils, 1 cm squared paper.

S5
Detour:
Shape puzzle

UA2ac/5

PSE
S/D2

Content

- Use of given 2D shapes to construct more complex shapes.

This is a variation on the well-known Tangram puzzle using a heart shape subdivided into seven pieces.

Detailed notes

Q1 Some pupils may need to be prompted to try turning pieces over to make the shapes on the page.

Q3 A wall display could be made using some of the shapes created by the pupils.

Equipment

Scissors, possibly glue.

S6
Detour:
Position fixing

UA3d/5
SM3a/4

PM/D3

Content

- Use of ordered number pairs to decode and encode
- Interpretation of information presented in visual form.

Detailed notes

Grid Ensure pupils understand how to interpret the grid and record the letter codes as ordered pairs.

Additional activity

Cross-code
Pupils should work in a group. Ask them to bring to school a printed crossword puzzle solution from a daily newspaper. They could use this to send messages to each other. Care will be needed as not all solutions show every letter of the alphabet, but pupils should quickly discover this for themselves. A display could be made of the crossword solutions brought in under the two categories

'Good for codes'   'Not good for codes'
with appropriate explanation attached to each solution. For example:
'This crossword solution was good to use for a code because it contains all the vowels of the alphabet.'

Equipment

None.

Content

- Interpretation of a calendar.

Successful completion of the work is dependent upon the pupils' ability to work methodically.

Introductory activity

Calendar

Pupils should recall or be given a copy of the rhyme '30 days has September, April, June and November. . .' There could also be a discussion on calendar facts. 'How do you know when it's a leap year?' 'What date is (a) Christmas Day, (b) Halloween, (c) Guy Fawkes Day?'

Detailed notes

Q2 Possible explanations could be that February had only 28 days or that (19)90 does not divide exactly by 4.

Q8 The difference between lunar and calendar or solar months could be discussed.

Q9 Pupils are expected to consult calendars for several different years including leap years.

Equipment

Calendars for several years including leap years.

S13
Detour:
Calendar

**UA3ad/4;
2c/5**

**PSE
I/C4**

Content

- Multiplication of whole numbers mentally and by calculator
- Using the strategies of looking for a pattern, making and testing a prediction.

A number investigation in which pairs of numbers, placed in opposite corners of squares within an addition square, are multiplied together and differences found.

Detailed notes

Q1a The completed table should be checked for accuracy by the teacher, the pupil or another pupil before proceeding further.

Q4a Discuss their previous results with the pupils. They should be asked to talk about their predictions. Many are likely to find it easier to talk rather than write about what they think.

Additional activity

Corners of rectangles

Some pupils may be able to investigate similar products and differences for rectangles, for example, of size 3 squares by 2 squares, drawn within the addition square. Can they predict for these rectangles? Is the rule for these rectangles different from their rule for squares?

Equipment

Calculator (for the more difficult multiplications only).

S21
Detour:
Number
investigation

**UA4b/4
A2b/4**

MD/C1

Content

Properties of number operations:

- the order in which numbers are added does not affect the sum
- addition can be used to check subtraction
- the order in which numbers are multiplied does not affect the product
- multiplication can be used to check division
- multiplication and addition can be used in combination to check a division with a remainder.

In investigating these properties pupils are required to make and test predictions.

Organisation

Pupils may benefit by discussing the questions in pairs.

Detailed notes

Q1,2 last line The number of calculations might be specified as, say, three.

Q3,4 Encourage the pupils to agree on an oral statement. This could be written as a wall poster and all the statements discussed to establish the best form of wording.

Q6 If pupils require help with finding the 'rule' suggest that they try to modify the multiplication check for division.

Q7 If working in pairs the check should be by another pair.

Equipment

A calculator may be used.

E9
Detour:
Checking
calculations

**UA4b/5
N3a, 4c/5**

PSE

31	32 W5 W6	33
Centimetres and inches	Length and money	Weight and money

CONTENT AND DEVELOPMENT

Core

Decimals 1 (on pages 13–19 of these notes) covers work on place value to hundredths, addition and subtraction of two-place decimals, multiplication of two-place decimals by 2 to 10 and 100, multiplication of two-place decimals by two- and three-digit whole numbers using the calculator.

Decimals 2 consolidates some of this work through the contexts of length, weight and money. It covers:

- conversion between centimetres and inches involving the multiplication of one-place decimals by a single-digit whole number
- addition and subtraction of two-place decimals.

Division of decimals is covered in these notes in *Division 1* and *Division 2* (see pages 55–59 and 77–80). *Decimals 3* (see pages 91–96) contains work on place value to thousandths and approximation to the first decimal place.

National Curriculum (England and Wales)

UA3b
N3c, 4ab
SM4ab
HD2a

Mathematics 5–14 (Scotland)

PSE
RTN/D4
AS/D2
MD/D3
ME/C6, D9

RELATED ACTIVITIES

See note for *Decimals 1*, on page 13 of these notes.

EQUIPMENT

Ruler, measuring tape.
For the Introductory activities: parcels with weights marked.

Content

- Interpretation of a conversion table
- Multiplication of one-place decimals by a single-digit whole number
- Practical measurement
- Relationship between inches and centimetres.

Organisation

Q2 and Q5 involve personal measurements and pupils should work in pairs for these activities. The measurements are also used in Core Textbook page 32 for W5 and W6.

Detailed notes

Q1 Ensure that units are correctly labelled.

Q3 'to the nearest $\frac{1}{2}$ cm' may need to be explained.

Q4 Pupils are expected to use the approximations given above.

Q5 Following the conversion calculation pupils should check their answer by measuring their height in centimetres.

Introductory activity

Which size?
Measurements given on clothes' labels and conversion charts displayed in shops and catalogues could be used as a basis for a discussion of metric and imperial units of measure.
Through the activities of this page pupils should become familiar with the approximations:
1 inch is about 2·5 cm, 1 foot is about 30 cm.

Equipment

Ruler, measuring tape.

31
Decimals 2:
Centimetres
and inches

N4ab/4
SM4a/5

RTN/D4
MD/D3
ME/D9

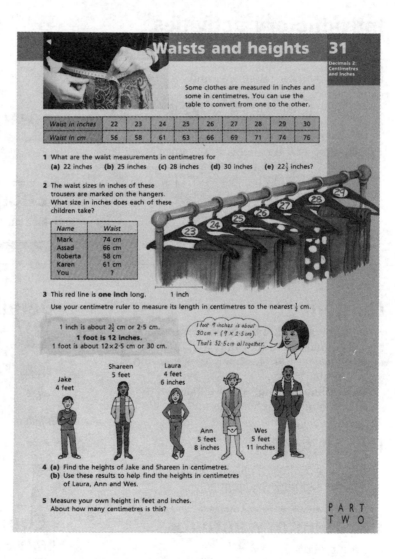

Waists and heights — 31

Decimals 2:
Centimetres
and inches

Some clothes are measured in inches and some in centimetres. You can use the table to convert from one to the other.

Waist in inches	22	23	24	25	26	27	28	29	30
Waist in cm	56	58	61	63	66	69	71	74	76

1 What are the waist measurements in centimetres for
(a) 22 inches (b) 25 inches (c) 28 inches (d) 30 inches (e) 22½ inches?

2 The waist sizes in inches of these trousers are marked on the hangers. What size in inches does each of these children take?

Name	Waist
Mark	74 cm
Assad	66 cm
Roberta	58 cm
Karen	61 cm
You	?

3 This red line is **one inch** long.   1 inch
Use your centimetre ruler to measure its length in centimetres to the nearest ½ cm.

1 inch is about 2½ cm or 2·5 cm.
1 foot is 12 inches.
1 foot is about 12 × 2·5 cm or 30 cm.

1 foot 9 inches is about 30 cm + (9 × 2·5 cm). That's 52·5 cm altogether.

Jake 4 feet
Shareen 5 feet
Laura 4 feet 6 inches
Ann 5 feet 8 inches
Wes 5 feet 11 inches

4 (a) Find the heights of Jake and Shareen in centimetres.
(b) Use these results to help find the heights in centimetres of Laura, Ann and Wes.

5 Measure your own height in feet and inches. About how many centimetres is this?

PART TWO

32
W5
W6
Decimals 2:
Length and
money

UA3b/5
N3c, 4ab/4
HD2a/4

RTN/D4
AS/D2

Content

- Interpretation of information presented in written and diagrammatic form
- Interpretation and completion of tables
- Addition of two-place decimals in money
- Practical measurement.

Organisation

See page 3 in these notes for information on the use of the Goodies catalogue. W5 Q1 involves practical measurement and pupils should work either with a partner or in small groups. The teams of six for W6 would be best formed by combining sets of partners who have worked together for W5. This would produce 'checks' as each team will require the same items since it is only the captain who changes.

Introductory activities

1 Catalogue references and items
Items from the catalogue Pages 70 and 71 can be identified by their references and *vice versa*. For example:
- (a) Which item has the catalogue reference CC1321?
  (Girl's jeans with waist 51 cm, 54 cm)
- (b) What is the catalogue reference and the cost of a sweatshirt for a person whose height is 125 cm?   (CC1420, £12·99)

2 Range of sizes
Discuss the correct selection of size from a given range of sizes for individual items, For example:
- (a) Pauline has a height of about 125 cm. Which size of sweatshirt should she order?
  (125 lies in the range 122/128 so the catalogue reference is CC1420.)
- (b) Tara has a height of about 130 cm. Which size should she choose?
  (130 does not lie within any of the stated ranges and so Tara would choose the next size, that is 134/140 cm CC1421.)

Detailed notes

Q1	Encourage pupils to record individual prices as well as the total.
Q2	Pupils should be familiar with the order forms, however, some pupils may need help.
W5, Q1	Height and waist measurements should be available from Core Textbook page 31. This information is also needed for W6.
W5, Q2	Pupils with measurements outside the catalogue range should invent a new size, reference number, price, etc.
W6, Q2	Order Form 9 could be extended if necessary, by attaching a ruled strip of paper to the bottom of the printed form.

Equipment

Measuring tape.

33
Decimals 2:
Weight and
money

UA3b/5
N3c/4
SM4ab/5

PSE
RTN/D4
AS/D2
ME/C6

Content

- Addition and subtraction of two-place decimals in money and weight
- Interpretation of a ready reckoner and circular scales
- Problem solving: working backwards
- Relationship between grams and kilograms.

Organisation

See page 3 of these notes for information on the use of the Goodies catalogue.

Introductory activity

Posting parcels
The table of postal charges will need careful discussion to establish the meaning of the phrase 'weight not over'. This could be done by producing a variety of parcels with weights clearly marked. For example:

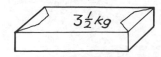

This parcel weighs $3\frac{1}{2}$ kg. How much would it cost to post?
Since the parcel is over 3 kg but under 4 kg the cost would be £3·40.

Detailed notes

Q2b,3b	Total weight must be found first.
Q4	Requires consideration of the Special Offer on Catalogue Page 69 and the free postage offer advertised on this page. There is bound to be discussion on whether both ways of saving money apply. The better deal is the free postage one in this case.
Q5	The offer price must be found first.

Equipment

For the Introductory activity: parcels with weights clearly marked.

34, 35

Approximate costs

CONTENT AND DEVELOPMENT

Core

Other methods 1 (on pages 8 and 9 of these notes) covers work on approximation to the nearest 100 and 1000 and the use of the Associative Law to find the easiest order of calculation using whole numbers.

This section looks at various methods of finding an estimate of a total cost for a number of items by

- rounding each item to the nearest pound
- rounding each item to the nearest 50p
- grouping items with prices which have an approximate sum of a number of pounds.

Other methods 3 (on pages 124 and 125 of these notes) contains work on multiplication and division by multiples of 10 and 100.

National Curriculum (England and Wales)

N3cf

Mathematics 5–14 (Scotland)

RTN/C3
AS/D2, D3
RN/D1

EQUIPMENT

Calculator.
For the Introductory activity: catalogue, shopping items.

34
35
Other methods 2: Approximate costs

N3c/4;
3f/5

RTN/C3
AS/D2, D3
RN/D1

Content

- Addition and subtraction of two-place decimals in money
- Estimation of a total cost by rounding individual prices to the nearest pound and to the nearest 50p
- Estimation of a total cost by grouping items with prices which have an approximate sum of a number of pounds.

Introductory activities

1 Pricing strategies
Discuss the pricing strategies used in shops, for example:
- £19·99, £19·95 to make the cost appear as £19 rather than £20
- £2·15 to make the cost just over £2, and so on.

Pupils could make a display of prices used in a catalogue, grouping together the prices which have the 'pence' in common for example, £2·99, £3·99, £5·99.

2 Estimating a total cost by rounding prices to the nearest pound
Establish by discussion that in real life pupils will need to approximate prices to check that they have enough money to pay for items chosen or that they haven't been overcharged.
It is possible to illustrate the concepts of rounding through a 'mock shop' using real items clearly priced, for example:
sauce 84p, nuts 23p, coffee £2·65, fish £1·21, hankies £1·14, soap powder £3·49, flour £1·51, yogurts £1·50.
Each price should first be rounded to the nearest pound, for example:
The price of the coffee is between £2 and £3 but is nearer £3. The coffee costs £3 rounded to the nearest pound.

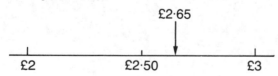

The price of the yogurts (£1·50) should be discussed emphasising that the rounded price can be either £1 or £2.
Once the prices have been rounded, the total estimated cost of buying the items can be calculated.

3 Estimating a total cost by rounding prices to the nearest 50p
The cost of each item in the 'mock shop' should be rounded to the nearest 50p.
For example, the price of the coffee is between £2·50 and £3.
It is nearer £2·50.

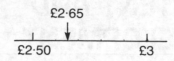

The coffee costs £2·50 rounded to the nearest 50p.
The total cost of buying the items should be estimated using the rounded prices.

4 Estimating a total cost by grouping
Items should be grouped which give a total of about a whole number of pounds for example:
sauce (84p) and fish (£1·21), estimated total cost is £2.
coffee (£2·65), nuts (23p) and hankies (£1·14), estimated total cost is £5.
The total cost of buying the items should be estimated using the rounded prices.

Detailed notes

Q3 Answers should be along these lines: 'to check the total', 'to check that you have enough money'.

Q12 Pupils should realise that it is possible for an estimate to be
- higher than the actual cost, so the cost may still be affordable
- lower than the actual cost, so that an item has to be put back.

Q13 Various items could be put back but encourage the choice of the item(s) which bring the total nearest the amount to spend.

Equipment

Calculator.
For the Introductory activities: catalogue, shopping items.

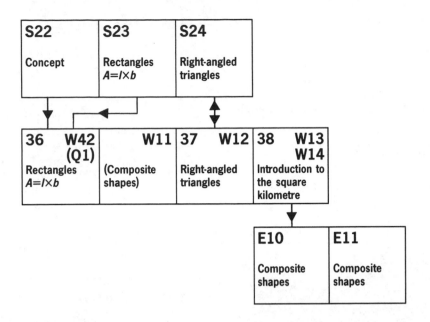

CONTENT AND DEVELOPMENT

Core

Pupils should already be able to find the area of a rectangle by counting squares. Some should be able to shorten this process by finding the number of squares in a row and multiplying this by the number of rows.

In *Area*, these ideas are consolidated and developed further to cover:

- area of a rectangle using the formula $A = l \times b$
- area of a right-angled triangle as half the area of its surrounding rectangle
- area of composite shapes made up of right-angled triangles and rectangles/squares
- area of shapes with a curved edge by counting squares and part squares
- use of larger units of area: square metre, hectare, square kilometre.

Support

S22 and S23 may be used either as lead-in pages or as support for Core Textbook page 36 and W42 and W11. S24 provides a lead-in or support for Core Textbook page 37. These three Support pages could also be used as parallel work, and as alternatives to the Core pages.

Extension

E10 and E11 could be attempted on completion of the Core Textbook pages or after W12 and before Core Textbook page 38.

National Curriculum (England and Wales)

SM4ad

Mathematics 5–14 (Scotland)

ME/C3, D4, E2, E5
PFS/E1
E+

EQUIPMENT

1 cm squared paper, plain paper, ruler, metre stick or tape, large sheets of paper or newspaper, sticky tape, calculator, atlas.
For the Introductory activities: prepared diagram, OHP transparency with squared grid, pair of card congruent right-angled triangles, squared paper, card rectangle, scissors, ruler.

36
W42
(Q1)
Area:
Rectangles
$A=l\times b$

SM4d/
4 → 6

ME/C3
PFS/E1

Content

- Area of a rectangle
  - by multiplying the number of rows by the number of squares in each row
  - by using the formula $A=l\times b$
- Construction of rectangles of specified areas.

Introductory activity

Area of rectangle
Draw a design and its surrounding rectangle on a square grid as shown.

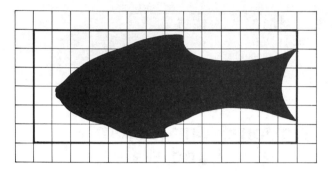

Discuss with the pupils a method of finding the area of the rectangle by counting squares even though some are hidden. Establish the method of counting the number of squares in one row and then multiplying this by the number of rows.

Detailed notes

| Q1 | Pupils may need to be reminded that the abbreviation for square centimetres is cm². |

| Q5 | Provide 1 cm squared paper. More able pupils should use plain paper and measure with a ruler. |

| W42, panel | Discuss with the pupils that finding the number of squares in one row is the same as finding the length and that finding the number of rows is the same as finding the breadth. The area of a rectangle can then be expressed as length times breadth or $A=l\times b$ |

Equipment

1 cm squared paper, plain paper, ruler.
For the Introductory activity: prepared diagram.

W11
Area:
Composite
shapes

SM4d/
5 → 6

PFS/E1

Content

- Areas of composite shapes made up of rectangles, using $A=l\times b$
- Construction of shapes with a given area.

Introductory activity

Shapes made up of rectangles
Composite shapes could be drawn on an OHP transparency. For example:

Pupils could then be asked to partition the shapes into rectangles, in at least two ways. For example:

can be partitioned as   and

The area should be calculated for both ways of partitioning to emphasise that the method of partitioning does not affect the total area of the shape.

Detailed notes

| Q2 | Pupils should not count squares but should use the formula. |

| Q4 | Pupils could discuss and check their answers in pairs. |

Equipment

1 cm squared paper, ruler.
For the Introductory activity: OHP transparency showing a squared grid.

Content

- Area of right-angled triangle as half the area of the surrounding rectangle
- Construction of right-angled triangles of specific area
- Area of composite shapes made up of right-angled triangles and rectangles/squares.

Introductory activities

1 Right-angled triangles
Show the pupils a pair of card congruent right-angled triangles to represent a pair of earrings. Through discussion highlight that:

- the earrings are identical in shape and area
- the two earrings can be placed side by side to create a rectangle
- each earring or right-angled triangle is half the area of the rectangle.

Suggest that if the area of a right-angled triangle is to be found, a second congruent right-angled triangle of equal area can be drawn to form a rectangle, as shown.

The area of the right-angled triangle is found as half of the area of the surrounding rectangle.

2 Composite shapes
This activity should be carried out before most pupils attempt W12. Draw a composite shape, for example:

Ask pupils how they might partition the shape into rectangles and right-angled triangles.

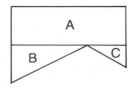

The area of each part should be recorded:
Area of rectangle A   =
Area of right-angled triangle B =
Area of right-angled triangle C =
Total area   =

Detailed notes

Panel above Q1	Discuss the fact that 6 and 3 are the length and breadth measurements (in cm) of the rectangle.
Q2	Measurements should be made to the nearest centimetre.
W12,Q1	The wording for the recording is only printed for (a). Pupils should write the steps for (b) and (c) themselves.
W12,Q3	Pupils might enjoy reproducing the brooches in card covered with foil or in coloured plastic sheeting.

Equipment

1 cm squared paper, ruler.
For the Introductory activities: a pair of card congruent right-angled triangles.

37
W12
Area:
Right-angled
triangles

SM4d/6

ME/D4
PFS/E1

Content

- Areas of larger surfaces
- Introduction to the square kilometre
- Areas of irregular shapes in m² and km²
- Estimation of areas shown in simple plans and maps
- Interpretation of information in pictorial form.

Organisation

The Introductory activity should be carried out on completion of Core Textbook page 38, Q3.

Introductory activity

Areas of irregular shapes
Ask pupils to draw a circle on squared paper using compasses set to a stated radius. To find the area of the circle, the method of counting whole squares and part squares should be discussed.

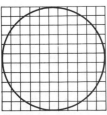

Detailed notes

Q1	One possibility is to cut four squares of side 50 cm and tape them together.
Q2	Pupils should use their square metre from Q1 as a template or they could measure out a rectangle using a metre stick or tape.
Q2b	Some pupils may need to be reminded that 50 cm is the same as half a metre.
W13,Q1	Pupils should partition the shapes into rectangles and right-angled triangles.
W13,Q2	Discuss with pupils the method for counting part squares as suggested in the Introductory activity.
W14, Q1c	Ask some pupils to describe orally how they made their estimate.

Equipment

Metre stick or tape, large sheet of paper or newspaper, sticky tape, calculator, atlas with a map of Scotland.
For the Introductory activity: squared paper.

38
W13
W14
Area:
Introduction
to the square
kilometre

SM4a/5;
4d/5 → 6

ME/E2, E5

Content

- Areas of shapes in cm² by counting squares
- Approximate areas of irregular shapes counting whole and part squares.

Detailed notes

Q2 After some pupils have attempted (a) and (b), discuss with the group what 'rule' should be used for counting the areas of part squares. Pupils may suggest one of these methods:

- count as whole squares those part squares equal or greater than half a square and ignore the rest

- perceptually combine part squares to form 'whole' squares and count these.

Pupils should realise that the first 'rule' is usually the more efficient.

Q3 Pupils may suggest the following 'funny shapes':

- any unusual shape
- shapes with curved edges
- shapes with part squares
- shapes like the snake in Q2(d).

All of these would be acceptable.

Equipment

1 cm squared paper.

S23
Area:
Rectangles
A — l×b

**SM4d/
4 → 6**

**ME/C3
PFS/E1**

Content

- Area of a rectangle
  - by multiplying the number of rows by the number of squares in each row or *vice versa*
  - by multiplying length by breadth
- Construction of rectangles of specified area.

Introductory activity

Area of rectangle
For details see the Introductory activity for Core Textbook page 36.

Equipment

1 cm squared paper.
For the Introductory activity: prepared diagram as used on Core Textbook page 36.

S24
Area:
Right-angled
triangles

**SM4d/
5 → 6**

**ME/D4
PFS/E1**

Content

- Area of right-angled triangle as half the area of the surrounding rectangle
- Construction of right-angled triangles of specific area.

Introductory activity

Half of a rectangle
Draw a diagonal on a card rectangle and cut the rectangle into two right-angled triangles. Place one triangle on top of the other to show that the whole rectangle has been divided into two equal parts. Establish that the area of the right-angled triangle is half of its surrounding rectangle.

Detailed notes

Q1,2 Encourage pupils to trace out the surrounding rectangle with their fingers, find the area of that rectangle and then halve it.

Q3 Some pupils may require help to realise that each rectangle should be *twice* the given area of the right-angled triangle.

Equipment

1 cm squared paper.
For the Introductory activity: card rectangle, scissors, ruler.

Content

- Areas of composite shapes made up of two or more rectangles
- Construction of composite shapes of specific area.

Detailed notes

Q3 Encourage pupils to make a rough sketch of examples (b) to (e) so that they can draw lines to show their subdivisions of each shape.

Q4 The letters should be made from rectangles, with the overall total area equal to 12 cm^2. The rectangles used are likely to be only one or two centimetres wide.

Equipment

1 cm squared paper, a ruler marked in centimetres.

E11
Area:
Composite
shapes

**SM4d/
5 → 6**

E+

Content

- Areas of composite shapes made up of rectangles and one or more right-angled triangles.

Detailed notes

Q3 Encourage pupils to make a rough sketch of each shape and to show their subdivisions.

Additional activity

Devising composite shapes
The pupils can be asked to draw, on 1 cm squared paper, four examples of composite shapes made up of rectangles and right-angled triangles. These should be given to a friend to find their total areas.

Equipment

For the Additional activity: 1 cm squared paper, a ruler marked in centimetres.

39	40	41
Equivalence	Halves and quarters, +, −	Halves and quarters, +, −

CONTENT AND DEVELOPMENT

Core

Previous work on fractions should have included the meaning of a fraction, equivalent fractions, fractions of a set and simple addition of halves and quarters.

In *Fractions 1*, the work is revised and extended to cover:

- one number as a fraction of another
- equivalent fractions and the use of equivalence in simplification
- addition and subtraction of halves and quarters.

Fractions 2 (on pages 84–86 of these notes) deals with multiplication of a fraction or a mixed number by a whole number and the calculation of a fraction of a whole number.

National Curriculum (England and Wales)

N2b, 3c

Mathematics 5–14 (Scotland)

RTN/E2

EQUIPMENT

For the Introductory activities: paper circles and/or squares, coloured pencils.

Content

- One number as a fraction of another
- Equivalent fractions
- Use of equivalence in the comparison and simplification of fractions.

Organisation

It is suggested that Q1 to Q3 be attempted after Introductory activity 1 and the remaining questions after Introductory activity 2.

Introductory activities

1 One number as a fraction of another
Revise this idea using simple practical activities:

- Lay out 4 black and 3 red pencils. Establish that there are 7 pencils altogether and since 4 out of the 7 are black, then $\frac{4}{7}$ are black.
- Ask some pupils to stand in front of the class. Establish how many are in the group and ask questions such as 'What fraction of the group are boys?' and so on.

2 Equivalent fractions
The idea of equivalence could be revised by

- folding and colouring paper shapes or using a fraction board drawn on the blackboard,

Paper circle

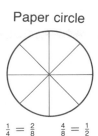

$\frac{1}{4} = \frac{2}{8}$ $\frac{4}{8} = \frac{1}{2}$

Fraction board

1 whole									
$\frac{1}{2}$					$\frac{1}{2}$				
$\frac{1}{5}$		$\frac{1}{5}$		$\frac{1}{5}$		$\frac{1}{5}$		$\frac{1}{5}$	
$\frac{1}{10}$	$\frac{1}{10}$	$\frac{1}{10}$	$\frac{1}{10}$	$\frac{1}{10}$	$\frac{1}{10}$	$\frac{1}{10}$	$\frac{1}{10}$	$\frac{1}{10}$	$\frac{1}{10}$

$\frac{1}{5} = \frac{2}{10}$ $\frac{5}{10} = \frac{1}{2}$

- discussing the illustrative panel relating to packs and cans of cola.

Remind pupils of the rules for generating equivalent fractions:
'Multiply numerator and denominator by the same number' *or*
'Divide numerator and denominator by the same number'.

Detailed notes

Q5 Compare the numerators or denominators of the fractions to find the appropriate multiplier in order to calculate the missing number.

Q9 The two aspects of the work on the page – expressing one number as a fraction of another and equivalence – are brought together here.

Equipment
None.

Content

- Addition and subtraction involving halves and quarters.

The examples involve mixed number additions in which the total of the fractional parts is ≤. There are also related mixed number subtraction examples.

The examples should be done mentally or by referring to the illustrative panels *and not by any formal written method*.

Introductory activity

Basic facts
Remind pupils of the basic addition and subtraction facts relating to halves and quarters as given in the 'Remember' panels. Do this by

- discussing the illustrative panels
- using a number line.

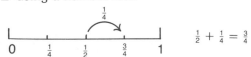

$\frac{1}{2} + \frac{1}{4} = \frac{3}{4}$

Pupils should then be given practice in mental addition and subtraction of mixed numbers involving halves and quarters as follows:

$2\frac{1}{2} + 3\frac{1}{4}$
$= 5\frac{3}{4}$

$2 + 3 = 5$
$\frac{1}{2} + \frac{1}{4} = \frac{3}{4}$

40
Fractions 1:
Halves and
quarters, +, −

N2b/4;
3c/5 → 6

RTN/E2

$6\frac{3}{4} - 2\frac{1}{4}$
$= 4\frac{1}{2}$

$6 - 2 = 4$
$\frac{3}{4} - \frac{1}{4} = \frac{1}{2}$

Detailed notes

Q4 Discuss the difficulty of examples of the type $8 - \frac{1}{4}$. Some pupils may visualise $\frac{1}{4}$ less than 8 on a number line giving $7\frac{3}{4}$. Others may think of 8 as 7 + 1 and then take $\frac{1}{4}$ from the 1 to give the answer $7\frac{3}{4}$.

Q6 The total weight of the items in the yellow box is 6 kg and in the white box $3\frac{3}{4}$ kg. The answer can be found as follows: 6 kg take away 3 kg gives 3 kg, then take away another $\frac{3}{4}$ kg to give $2\frac{1}{4}$ kg.

Equipment
None.

Content

- Addition and subtraction involving halves and quarters.

The examples involve mixed number additions in which the total of the fractional parts is >1. There are also related mixed number subtraction examples.

The examples should be done by 'counting on' or 'counting back' using the illustrated number lines if necessary. The key facts which are needed to support this method are

$\frac{1}{2} = \frac{1}{4} + \frac{1}{4}$ and $\frac{3}{4} = \frac{1}{2} + \frac{1}{4}$ or $\frac{3}{4} = \frac{1}{4} + \frac{1}{2}$

No formal written method should be used.

Introductory activity

Counting on/back on a number line
Use the following examples to discuss the methods of 'counting on' or 'counting back'.

(a) $2\frac{3}{4} + \frac{1}{2}$ Consider $\frac{1}{2}$ as $\frac{1}{4} + \frac{1}{4}$.
$\frac{1}{4}$ is added to $2\frac{3}{4}$ to give the whole number 3.
The remaining $\frac{1}{4}$ is added to 3 to give the answer $3\frac{1}{4}$.

(b) $6\frac{1}{2} - \frac{3}{4}$ Consider $\frac{3}{4}$ as $\frac{1}{2} + \frac{1}{4}$.
$\frac{1}{2}$ is subtracted from $6\frac{1}{2}$ to give the whole number 6.
The remaining $\frac{1}{4}$ is subtracted from 6 to give the answer $5\frac{3}{4}$.

(c) $1\frac{1}{2} + 2\frac{3}{4}$ Add the whole number 2 (from $2\frac{3}{4}$) to $1\frac{1}{2}$ to give $3\frac{1}{2} + \frac{3}{4}$.
Proceed as for (a).

(d) $7\frac{1}{4} - 1\frac{1}{2}$ Subtract the whole number 1 (from $1\frac{1}{2}$) from $7\frac{1}{4}$ to give $6\frac{1}{4} - \frac{1}{2}$.
Proceed as for (b).

Detailed notes

Q1,2,3 A fraction has to be added to or taken from a mixed number.

Q4,5,6 Addition or subtraction of two mixed numbers. Although no formal written method is expected, many pupils may be helped by inserting an intermediate step when recording their answers.
For example: $2\frac{1}{2} + 3\frac{3}{4}$
$= 5\frac{1}{2} + \frac{3}{4}$
$= 6\frac{1}{4}$

Equipment

None.

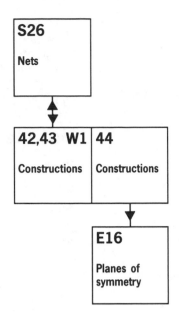

CONTENT AND DEVELOPMENT

Core

Following earlier 3D shape work pupils should be able to identify and name certain shapes including cube, cuboid, sphere, prism and pyramid.

3D shape emphasises the construction of a range of 3D shapes and covers:

- construction of nets
- use of those nets to make 3D models by combining prisms and pyramids.

Some shapes are introduced which are likely to be new to the pupils: stellated cube, hexahedron, octahedron, dodecahedron, icosahedron, truncated tetrahedron, and stellated dodecahedron.

Support

S26 can be used as an alternative for pupils who find the construction methods in the Core Textbook pages too demanding.

Extension

E16 could be done on completion of the Core Textbook pages.

National Curriculum (England and Wales)

SM2abc

Mathematics 5–14 (Scotland)

RS/E4
E+

RELATED ACTIVITIES

Decorations and gift boxes
Pupils could make other shapes using the construction methods in this section. These shapes could be used as Christmas decorations or as gift boxes.

EQUIPMENT

Paint, 1 cm squared and 1 cm isometric paper, sticky tape, coloured felt pens or pencils, paper clips, card, scissors, glue, templates made using W1, at least forty 2p coins.

Content

- Construction of 3D and composite 3D shapes by
  - making templates of 2D shapes
  - making a supply of 2D shapes using these templates
  - constructing a net using the 2D shapes.

Organisation

Divide the pupils into four groups. The work should be shared within each group.

Introductory activities

1 Making a template
The diagram on W1 can be used for making a template, as follows:

- place W1 on top of a sheet of card
- secure them together using paper-clips
- use a pin to prick through at the corners of the template being made
- join the pin-holes on the card with straight lines
- cut out the template.

The instructions, given on W1, demonstrate how a template (of an isosceles triangle) which is not drawn on the page can be made by identifying the appropriate corners.

2 Assembly of a net
Show pupils a net and discuss how to join the edges by:

- using sticky tape
- identifying where flaps would be useful and drawing these before cutting out the net.

Detailed notes

| Q1 for all groups | Pupils should be encouraged to list the shape of templates and the number of each required for their task. |
| State-ment below Q3 | The models made by two or more groups could be used to make mobiles. |

Equipment

Templates made from card, scissors, glue, paint or coloured felt pens, sticky tape, paper clips.

Content

- Construction of 3D shapes with eight or more faces.

The work is similar to that on Core Textbook pages 42 and 43 but is at a more demanding level.

Organisation

Five groups could be formed and the constructions allocated as follows:

Group 1 – regular octahedron and two pentagonal pyramids.
Group 2 – regular dodecahedron and two pentagonal pyramids.
Group 3 – regular icosahedron and two pentagonal pyramids.
Group 4 – truncated tetrahedron and two pentagonal pyramids.
Group 5 – regular dodecahedron and four pentagonal pyramids.

Group 5 can make a stellated dodecahedron using the pentagonal pyramids produced by the other groups.

Equipment

Templates used for pages 42 and 43, card, sticky tape, glue, scissors, paint or coloured felt pens.

Content

- Drawing nets on square and triangular grid paper
- Construction of a cuboid and a triangular prism using the nets.

Organisation

Pupils could work in pairs to make one of each shape.

Additional activity

Other boxes
Design a net for a cuboid to hold, for example, a calculator, or the net for a triangular prism to hold 5p coins.

Equipment

Card, 1 cm squared and 1 cm isometric paper, glue, scissors, coloured pencils or felt pens, sticky tape, at least forty 2p coins.

Detailed notes

Q1a Explain to pupils that in this instance 'identical' means having the same shape and size. The completed box should have opposite faces the same colour.

Q1b Pupils might be helped to find the missing lengths if they first mark 'base' and 'lid' on the sketch of the net as shown.

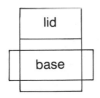

They can then visualise the net folded into the box shape and compare with the drawing of the box.

Q1c The net should be drawn on an A4 sheet of 1 cm squared paper.

Q1d, 2b Having glued the net on card, fold lines should be scored so that when the box is made, the squared paper is on the inside. Sticky tape can then be used to join the edges of the box.

Q2d The box should hold about thirty-nine 2p coins when placed flat, one on top of the other.

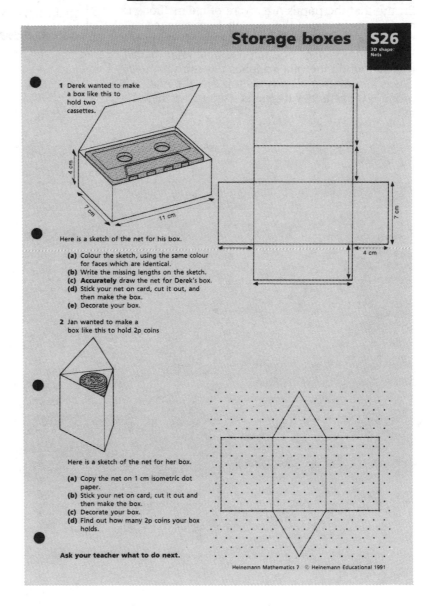

Storage boxes S26
3D shape: Nets

1 Derek wanted to make a box like this to hold two cassettes.

Here is a sketch of the net for his box.

(a) Colour the sketch, using the same colour for faces which are identical.
(b) Write the missing lengths on the sketch.
(c) **Accurately** draw the net for Derek's box.
(d) Stick your net on card, cut it out, and then make the box.
(e) Decorate your box.

2 Jan wanted to make a box like this to hold 2p coins

Here is a sketch of the net for her box.

(a) Copy the net on 1 cm isometric dot paper.
(b) Stick your net on card, cut it out and then make the box.
(c) Decorate your box.
(d) Find out how many 2p coins your box holds.

Ask your teacher what to do next.

Heinemann Mathematics 7 © Heinemann Educational 1991

E16
3D Shape:
Planes of
symmetry

SM2ab/
4 → 5;
2c/5

RS/E4
E+

Content

- Construction of 3D shapes from nets
- Identification of planes of symmetry.

Organisation

Pupils should work in pairs. This facilitates the construction of 3D shapes and reduces the amount of time needed to complete the work.

Introductory activity

Making shapes from nets
Ensure that the pupils are aware of the methods to be used for drawing the nets on 1 cm squared paper and thereafter constructing the 3D shapes. When joining edges one pupil should hold them together while the other applies the sticky tape. When joining two 3D shapes together the end product looks better if glue is used rather than tape.

Additional activity

Planes of symmetry
There should be some, discussion to reinforce the meaning of *'plane of symmetry'*.
This type of 'balance' could be explored

- in other geometric shapes such as a cuboid or a square-based pyramid
- in classroom objects.

Equipment

1 cm squared paper, card, scissors, glue, sticky tape, coloured pencil (green preferred).

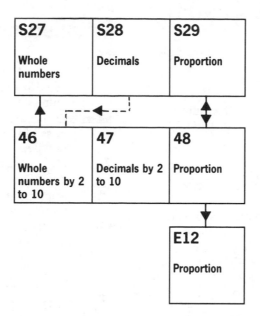

S27 Whole numbers	S28 Decimals	S29 Proportion
46 Whole numbers by 2 to 10	47 Decimals by 2 to 10	48 Proportion

E12 Proportion

CONTENT AND DEVELOPMENT

Core

Previous work on division should have included division of whole numbers, one- and two-place decimals by 2 to 10, 100 and two-digit whole numbers using paper and pencil techniques and a calculator, interpretation of the answer to a division problem, approximation to the appropriate whole number, approximation to the nearest unit, 10, 100 and 1000.

Division 1 consolidates some of this work and introduces proportion. It covers:

- division of whole numbers by 2 to 10
- division of one- and two-place decimals by 2 to 10
- proportion – unitary method.

The language and recording recommended for division is described on page T2 of these notes.

Division 2 (on pages 77–80 of these notes) covers work on division by two-digit whole numbers using a calculator, interpretation of a calculator display in context, calculation of the remainders in division problems, approximation to the nearest whole number.

Support

The Support material parallels the work of the Core Textbook and may be used as either lead-in or alternative material.

Extension

This extends the work on proportion using the calculator and should be attempted after completion of the Core material.

National Curriculum (England and Wales)

N3bce, 4a

Mathematics 5–14 (Scotland)

RTN/C1, C3, D4
MD/D1, D2, D3, D4
FPR/D1

EQUIPMENT

Calculator.
For the Introductory activities: multipacks of items displaying the number of items and the cost/weight, etc. of the pack.

46
Division 1:
Whole
numbers by 2
to 10

N3b/4

RTN/C1
MD/D1, D2,
D3
FPR/D1

Content

- Interpretation of information in written and diagrammatic form
- Division of whole numbers to thousands by 2 to 10
- Calculation of fractions of a whole number
- Interpretation of the answer to division problems in context.

Introductory activity

Revision of written technique
A variety of examples should be discussed with the class to reveal possible difficulties, for example:

- no exchange and with/without remainders $6843 \div 2$
- with exchange and with/without remainders $7135 \div 5$
- zeros in either the dividend or quotient $720 \div 4$ $624 \div 3$ $4905 \div 7$
- notation $3625 \div 5$ $\frac{1}{5}$ of 3625 $5\overline{)3625}$

Detailed notes

Q1 Some help with interpretation may be required. 'registration' has been used to avoid possible confusion between 'number plate' and 'lucky numbers'.

Q2 Ensure each number is checked as it is possible for more than one of the given numbers to win.

Q3 Use of fraction notation may cause difficulty.

Q6a Appropriate interpretation of the remainder is required.

Q6b Multiplication as well as division is required.

Equipment
None.

47
Division 1:
Decimals by 2
to 10

N3c/5

RTN/D4
MD/D2, D3

Content

- Interpretation of information in written form
- Division of one- and two-place decimals by 2 to 10
- Calculation of an average
- Relationship between hours and minutes, metres and centimetres.

Introductory activities

1 Revision of written technique
A variety of examples should be discussed with the class to reveal possible difficulties, for example:

- no exchange $63 \cdot 69 \div 3$
- with exchange $623 \cdot 5 \div 5$
- zeros in either the dividend or quotient $0 \cdot 48 \div 6$ $7 \cdot 02 \div 6$ $60 \cdot 9 \div 3$
- notation $36 \cdot 25 \div 5$ $\frac{1}{5}$ of $36 \cdot 25$ $5\overline{)36 \cdot 25}$

2 Working beyond the given place value
Discuss examples where it is necessary to divide beyond the final place of the dividend to achieve an exact quotient. Choose examples where the quotient terminates at or before the second decimal place. Pupils should insert additional zeros as the calculation progresses. For example:

$$4\overline{)27} \quad 4\overline{)27 \cdot {}^30} \quad 4\overline{)27 \cdot {}^30} \quad 4\overline{)27 \cdot {}^30{}^20}$$
$$6 \qquad 6 \cdot \qquad 6 \cdot 7 \qquad 6 \cdot 7 5$$

A variety of examples should be included, for example:

$$208 \div 5 \quad 17 \cdot 4 \div 4 \quad 90 \div 8$$

Detailed notes

Q3 Pupils should work in pounds.

Q4 Some pupils may need reminding about how to find an average.

Q6 Pupils should work in minutes.

Q7a Some pupils may not give the answer in metres and centimetres.

Q7b Pupils should work in centimetres.

Equipment
None.

Content

- Interpretation and construction of proportion tables
- Use of division and multiplication to solve problems involving direct proportion.

Organisation

After Introductory activity 1, pupils should attempt Q1, 2 and 3. Pupils' responses to Q3 provide the lead-in to Introductory activity 2, after which pupils should complete the work of the page.

Introductory activities

1 Finding the cost/weight, etc. of one item
Show a pack of items, for example: 6 cakes costing 84p. Ask pupils to calculate the cost of one cake using the normal written method then introduce the tabular layout.

Number of cakes	Cost in pence
6	84
1	84 ÷ 6 = 14

The cost of one cake is 14p.

This activity should be repeated using several examples, concentrating initially on the process using whole numbers before using examples involving decimals. Ensure pupils can choose the correct headings for each table.
Possible examples are:
- 4 bars of chocolate weigh 134 grams. What is the weight of 1 bar?
- 8 ribbons have a total length of 226·4 cm. What is the length of each ribbon?

2 Finding the cost/weight, etc. of several items
Discuss the method used to find the answers to Q3. Develop the method of dividing to find the length of one lap and then multiplying to find the length of several laps.
Show how to extend the proportion table as illustrated in the panel below Q3.

Equipment

For the Introductory activities: packs of items displaying number of items and the cost/weight, etc.

Detailed notes

Q3 This question serves as an introduction to the Final Panel method of recording shown in the panel below Q3. First the distance travelled in 1 lap is found. Then the distances travelled in 2, 3 and 5 laps can be found by multiplication.

Q4 Ensure pupils understand the method of recording in the illustrative panel above Q4.

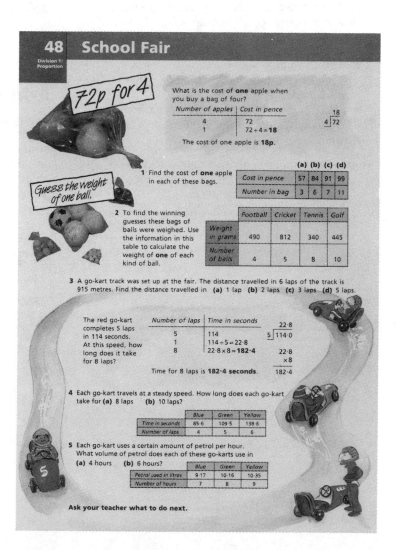

S27
Division 1:
Whole
numbers

N3b/4

RTN/C3
MD/D3

Content

- Exact division of two- and three-digit whole numbers by a single digit.

Introductory activity

Division of whole numbers by a single digit
Graded examples should be worked through using the butcher scenario, for example:

- without exchange –
  Beefburgers are packed in trays of six. How many trays are needed for 366 beefburgers?
- with exchange –
  Pork chops are packed in fives. How many packs can be made from 425 chops?
- with zeros in either dividend or quotient –
  Sirloin steaks are packed in fours. How many packs can be made from 304 steaks?
  Fillet steaks are packed in threes. How many packs can be made from 312 steaks?

Detailed notes

Q2 The conversion to pence may need to be discussed with some pupils.

Q3 Some help with interpretation may be required.

Equipment
None.

S28
Division 1:
Decimals

N3c/5

RTN/C3
MD/D3

Content

- Exact division of one- and two-place decimals by a single digit
- Calculation of an average.

Introductory activity

Division of decimals by a single digit
Graded examples should be worked through using the butcher scenario, for example:

- no exchange –
  4 steaks cost £8·44. What is the cost of one?
- with exchange –
  3 packs of mince weigh 7·32 kg. What is the weight of one pack?
- zeros in either the dividend or quotient –
  2 chickens cost £8·06. What is the cost of one?

Detailed notes

Q1a Emphasise that answers are in pounds.

Q1b The egg and fried tomato on the menus may confuse some pupils. Discuss the fact that as these items are common to both menus there is no need to know their costs. Pupils may work in either pounds or pence.

Q2c Some pupils may need reminding about how to calculate an average. The weekend should be interpreted as Saturday and Sunday.

Additional activity

Supermarket search
Pupils could collect clean trays and pack labels from supermarket items which could be used to find the cost/weight, etc. of one in each pack. Answers may need to be rounded to the nearest penny.

Equipment
None.

Content

- Interpretation and construction of proportion tables
- Use of division to solve problems involving direct proportion.

Organisation

After Introductory activity 1 pupils should attempt Q1 and Q2. Introductory activity 2 should then take place after which pupils should complete the work of the page.

Introductory activities

1 Multipacks
Find the cost/weight, etc. of one in a multipack.
For example:
A twin bar of chocolate cost 42p. What is the cost of one bar?

2 bars cost 42p. 1 bar costs $42 \div 2 = 21$p

2 Tabular layout
Introductory activity 1 for Core Textbook page 48 could be repeated using the data from Q1 and Q2 on S29 with pupils this time concentrating on the tabular layout rather than on the process.

Equipment

For the Introductory activities: packs of items displaying number of items and the cost/ weight, etc.

Content

- Interpretation of written information
- Interpretation and construction of proportion tables
- Use of the unitary method of proportion to solve problems.

Detailed notes

Q1 Encourage pupils to use the tabular layout for recording answers.

Panel after Q2 This is a two-stage calculation and a more efficient use of the calculator is shown. Pupils who use this method should alter the tabular layout accordingly.

Weight in kg	Pay in £
12	1·92
1	1·92 ÷ 12
14	(1·92 ÷ 12) × 14 = 2·24

Q3 This provides practice in consecutive division and multiplication where the calculator display is not cleared between operations.

Equipment

Calculator.

49	50	51	W16
Types of angles	Horizontal and vertical	Parallel and perpendicular	The shortest distance

CONTENT AND DEVELOPMENT

Core

Previous work on angles covered clockwise and anticlockwise turns, right, acute, obtuse, straight and reflex angles, measuring and constructing angles to the nearest ten degrees, bearings and parallel lines.

Angles 1 revises and extends some of this work and covers:

- right, acute, obtuse, straight and reflex angles, the sum of the angles of a triangle
- horizontal and vertical lines
- parallel and perpendicular lines
- shortest distance between a point and a line, including scale work.

Angles 2 (on pages 97–100 of these notes) extends the work on bearings and measurement and also construction of angles.

National Curriculum (England and Wales)

UA2abc, 3abc
SM2d

Mathematics 5–14 (Scotland)

PSE
ME/E1
PFS/E3
A/C1, C2, C3, E, E1, E3, E4

EQUIPMENT

Ruler, set square, scissors, shapes for tiling, material for making a plumb line and a spirit level, straws and either pipe-cleaners or sticky tape.
For the Introductory activities: jointed rods, set of prepared cardboard angles.

Content

- Right, acute, obtuse, straight and reflex angles
- Sum of the angles of a triangle
- Investigation of tiling properties of geometrical shapes.

Introductory activities

1 Jointed rods and cardboard corners
Pupils could position two jointed rods to show different angles. Alternatively you could use the jointed rods to show various types of angle which the pupils have to identify. You could also use a set of cardboard corners to show types of angles.

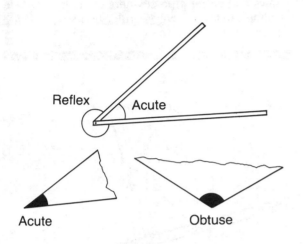

2 Angles in the environment
Discuss angles between the hands of a clock at different times. Ask pupils to make different types of angle with parts of their bodies. For example, at the elbow make acute, right, obtuse and straight angles. Pupils could also look for angles made by edges of furniture, etc.

3 Compass directions
Remind pupils of the compass directions. It may be worthwhile letting someone use an actual compass to find the direction of North in the classroom. Pupils may be interested to know that at mid-day GMT in Britain, the Sun is due South.

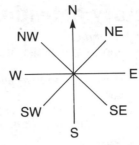

Discuss the type of angle between different compass directions:
an acute angle between N and NW, E and SE
an obtuse angle between E and SW, W and NE
and so on.

Detailed notes

Q2 The drawings of 3D objects may cause problems for some pupils.

Q5 As the octagon is the only shape that does not tile on its own, some teachers may prefer to omit it. Other shapes could be used for tilings if they are available.

Equipment

Scissors, shapes for tiling.
For Introductory activity 1: jointed rods, set of prepared cardboard angles.

49
Angles 1:
Types of angles

UA2b,
3ac/4
SM2d/5

PSE
A/C1, C2,
C3, E1, E4

Content

- Recognition of horizontal and vertical surfaces and lines
- Construction of an improvised plumb line and spirit level.

Introductory activity

Horizontal and vertical
Discuss horizontal and vertical lines and surfaces within
(a) *the classroom*, for example: desk top, window sill, door, blackboard and so on.
(b) *the environment*, for example: snooker table, ice rink, water in a swimming pool and so on.
Discuss the importance of horizontal and vertical in buildings and why some parts of buildings are neither horizontal nor vertical, for example, roofs and gutters. It would be of interest to mention that countries which have a lot of snow usually have very steep roofs.

Detailed notes

Picture above Q1 The objects in the drawing have to be interpreted in three dimensions.

Q6 Pupils should work in small groups and test the instruments they make to see how well they work on surfaces within the classroom.

Equipment

Material for making the plumb line and spirit level. For example, string, weights, ball, box and so on.

50
Angles 1:
Horizontal and vertical

UA2abc/5
SM2d/
4 → 5

PSE
A/E

51
Angles 1:
Parallel and
perpendicular

**SM2d/
4 → 5**

A/E3

Content

- Construction and identification of parallel lines
- Relationship between horizontal, vertical, parallel and perpendicular lines.

Introductory activities

1 Parallel and perpendicular
Discuss parallel and perpendicular in relation to everyday life.
Parallel: railway lines, slats in a Venetian blind and so on.
Perpendicular: streets of New York, T-junctions, T-squares, floor and walls in a room and so on.

2 Constructions
Give each pupil a ruler and set square and allow him/her to investigate the construction of parallel and perpendicular lines. After a reasonable amount of time demonstrate the methods indicated in the diagrams below.

Detailed notes

Q3 Discussion point: once the straws are fixed at right angles (perpendicular) to each other, ask a pupil to hold them so that
- one straw is vertical
- both straws are horizontal
- neither straw is vertical.

Map above Q4 Some pupils may require help with the interpretation of the map.

Equipment

Straws and either pipe-cleaners or sticky tape. For Introductory activity 2: ruler and set square.

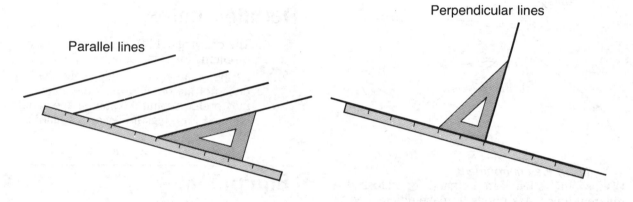

Parallel lines

Perpendicular lines

W16
Angles 1:
The shortest
distance

SM2d/5

**ME/E1
PFS/E3**

Content

- The shortest distance from a point to a line
- Use of a set square to draw perpendicular lines
- Interpretation and application of a scale.

Introductory activity

Shortest distance
Ask 5 pupils to stand in a straight line. Position another pupil (Jan) in front of one of the pupils in the line as shown.

Jan

Discuss which pupil is nearer to Jan. Repeat this for Jan in several positions. Establish that the shortest distance is the perpendicular distance.

Detailed notes

Q3 Some pupils may require further practice in constructing perpendicular lines.

Q4 Some pupils may need help to apply the scale factor.

Equipment

Ruler, set square.

52	53
Multiplication by two digits (pencil and paper)	Division by two digits (pencil and paper)

CONTENT AND DEVELOPMENT

Core

Whole numbers 1 (on pages 1–7 of these notes) contains work on approximation to the nearest 10, 100 and 1000, interpretation of reference numbers, addition and subtraction (up to four digits), multiplication by 2 to 10, 100 and two-digit whole numbers, division by 2 to 10.

Whole numbers 2 extends the pencil and paper work on multiplication and division. It covers:

- multiplication of a two- and three-digit whole number by a two-digit number
- division of three- and four-digit whole numbers by a two-digit whole number.

National Curriculum (England and Wales)

N3b

Mathematics 5–14 (Scotland)

MD/E1, E3
PFS/E1
E+

EQUIPMENT

None.

52

Whole
numbers 2:
Multiplication
by two digits
(pencil and
paper)

N3b/5

PFS/E1
E+

Content

- Calculation of areas of rectangles in square metres
- Multiplication by two-digit whole number without a calculator
- Multiplication by multiples of 10
- Multiplication of money by a whole number.

Introductory activities

Different non-standard methods of multiplication could be demonstrated.

1 Distributive Law

$$13 \times 24 = 13(20 + 4)$$
$$= 13 \times 20 + 13 \times 4$$
$$= 260 + 52$$
$$= 312$$

or $13 \times 24 = 13(4 + 20)$
$$= 13 \times 4 + 13 \times 20$$
$$= 52 + 260$$
$$= 312$$

2 Grid method
This can be explained using areas as shown.
For example, 47×24

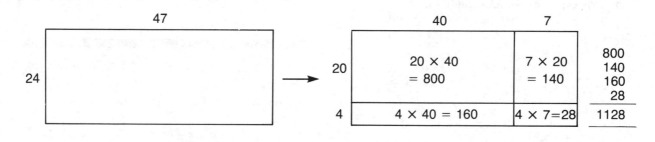

Detailed notes

Q4 Pupils should work in pence and convert their answers to pounds.

Additional activity

Other non-standard methods of multiplication could be explored. For example, Russian or Peasant multiplication, Napiers Rods, etc.

Equipment
None.

53

Whole
numbers 2:
Division by
two digits
(paper and
pencil)

N3b/5

MD/E1, E3
E+

Content

- Multiplication of two-digit whole numbers by 10, 100 and multiples of 10, 100
- Division of three- and four-digit whole numbers by a two-digit whole number, without a calculator.

Introductory activity

Recording form for division
'Mark's method', shown on this page, is the recording form which pupils are expected to know. A full description of this method is given on page T2 of these notes.

It is recommended that preliminary teaching is carried out to revise

- multiplication of two-digit numbers by 10 and multiples of 10
- 'Marks method' for division.

This could be done by setting the scene for Greenfingers Nursery using examples similar to the one at the top of the page, for example,
731 marigolds in 17 rows,
936 scented stock in 36 rows.
Pupils should be challenged to suggest how the number of subtractions might be reduced, leading to 'Dianne's method'.

Detailed notes

Q1 Working in pairs pupils could each do two examples using each method thus together doing all four examples by both methods. They could then discuss the number of subtractions used.

Q4 Since four-digit dividends are used here it may be necessary to revise multiplication by 100 and 200.

Equipment
None.

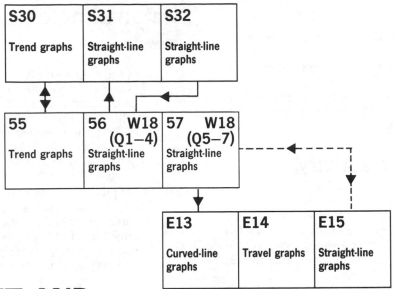

CONTENT AND DEVELOPMENT

Core

Handling data 1 (on pages 26–31 of these notes) covered interpretation and construction of bar graphs, combined bar graphs and also pie charts, calculation of range and mean, collection and organisation of data. Data based on measurement is rounded and in effect treated as discrete.

In this section, earlier work is consolidated and new work covers:

- interpretation and construction of line graphs in 'trend' graph form
- interpretation and construction of constant gradient straight-line graphs
- construction and use of straight-line graphs as 'conversion' (ready-reckoner) graphs
- interpretation of intermediate points between plotted points representing observed data.

Handling data 3 (on pages 135–138 of these notes) deals with the use of frequency tables and frequency diagrams with class intervals.

Graphs are also used where appropriate in other sections throughout the course.

Support

S30 is linked with Core Textbook page 55. S31 and S32 are linked with Core Textbook pages 56, and 57 and W8 either as lead-in or support work for those who have difficulty within the Core. Alternatively S30–S32 could be used by the least able as a parallel section to the Core.

Extension

E13–E15 may be used in any order following successful completion of the Core pages. E15 may be linked with Core Textbook page 57. New ideas include

- interpretation and construction of curved-line graphs
- interpretation and construction of travel graphs
- two straight-line graphs shown in the same diagram.

National Curriculum (England and Wales)

A2c
SM4d
HD2acf

Mathematics 5–14 (Scotland)

| C/E1 | O/C2, D1 |
| D/E1 | I/D1, E2 |

RELATED ACTIVITIES

Using a microcomputer

The construction by pupils of their own graphs has been emphasised. Some pupils will still experience difficulty in drawing an accurate graph with appropriate scales making the best use of the available squared paper. Many programs exist for microcomputers which can print a range of graphs from data input by the user. Pupils usually enjoy producing graphs in this way and these could be used both for wall display and as a basis for further discussion.

EQUIPMENT

2 mm, $\frac{1}{2}$ cm, 1 cm squared paper, 1 cm isometric dot paper, ruler, thermometer to measure outside temperature, string or thread. For an Introductory activity: travel company brochures containing weather information.

55
Handling
data 2:
Trend graphs

HD2acf/4

C/E1
O/D1
D/E1
I/D1, E2

Content

- Interpretation and construction of trend graphs
- Collection of temperature data and its display as a trend graph.

The term *trend graph* is used for line graphs which show how data has been changing over a period of time.

Introductory activity

Temperature variation
Discuss with the class or group how
- the temperature outside varies continuously, being lowest at night and highest in daytime
- the temperature outside varies with the seasons, being lowest in winter and highest in summer
- in the UK the temperature at noon may vary from around 0°C in winter to around 25°C in summer.

Detailed notes

Graphs Ensure pupils realise that the line joining the points in both graphs should *not* be used to read off the temperature at any other time. Because of this the points have been joined with broken lines which show the *trend* in the temperatures at noon. It is, however, common for the points to be joined with continuous lines and this form appears in Heinemann Mathematics 8.

Q6 Pupils should work in pairs to measure noon temperatures and make special arrangements for Saturday and Sunday readings. Data can also be collected from newspapers for other places in the country for comparison.

Equipment

2 mm squared paper, thermometer to measure outside temperatures.

56
W18
(Q1-4)
Handling
data 2:
Straight-line
graphs

A2c/5
HD2cf/5

O/D1
D/E1
I/D1

Content

- Interpretation and construction of constant gradient straight-line graphs
- Interpretation of intermediate points between plotted points representing observed data.

Introductory activity

Linking bar-line and straight-line graphs
Discuss the 'Cruising Around' scenario including the fact that *Kitty* cruises 'at a steady speed of 16 km per hour'.

Use the information above to construct a time/distance table and then a bar-line graph.

Time in hours	0	$\frac{1}{2}$	1	$1\frac{1}{2}$	2	$2\frac{1}{2}$
Distance in km	0	8	16	24	32	40

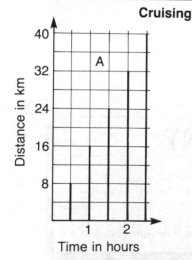
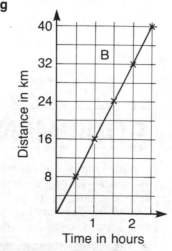

Further discussion should emphasise that
- as *Kitty* is travelling at a steady speed it covers equal distances in equal time intervals. Therefore the increase in lengths between adjacent bars is the same each time (graph A)

- when the lengths of adjacent bars increase in equal amounts the crosses marking the tops of the bars lie in a straight line (graph B)
- the points on the straight line *between* the crosses are meaningful. For example, in $1\frac{1}{4}$ hours the distance travelled is 20 km. The straight-line graph on page 56 is, effectively, the same as graph B.

Detailed notes

Q4b Discussion should highlight that
- only two points *need* to be plotted to draw a straight-line graph
- the two points chosen should be reasonably far apart to minimise error
- it is advisable to plot a third point and check that it too lies on the line. On $\frac{1}{2}$ cm squared paper a suitable scale is '1 small interval represents 5 km'.

W18, Q1b Suitable scales are
Volume axis: 1 small interval represents 2 litres
Cost axis: 1 small interval represents £1.

W18, Q2b Difficulties may arise because 75 litres does not fall on a grid line.

W18, Q3b Difficulties may arise because the volume costing £34 does not fall on a grid line.

Equipment

$\frac{1}{2}$ cm squared paper, ruler.

Content

- Interpretation and construction of straight-line graphs.

Two graphs are of the 'ready-reckoner' type and are referred to as conversion graphs.

Additional activity

Imperial units

The lower graph on W18 relates litres and gallons. There could be some further discussion concerning Imperial units used for measuring volume, for example:

- 8 pints is equivalent to 1 gallon
- 1 pint is just over $\frac{1}{2}$ litre.

57
W18
(Q5-7)
Handling data 2: Straight-line graphs

A2c/5
HD2cf/5

D/E1
I/D1

Equipment

Ruler.

Detailed notes

Q1 Remind pupils why three equivalent temperatures have been plotted. Explain that the straight line does *not* pass through the origin and that intermediate points on the straight line are meaningful.

Q7 Contrast the direction of the slope of this graph with previous graphs which have been concerned with uniform *increase* and consequently have sloped *upwards* from left to right. This graph is concerned with uniform *decrease* and consequently slopes *downwards* from left to right.

Q8 Pupils may have difficulty working out that each small interval represents 6 minutes.

Q10c Discuss different ways of calculating the average speed.
- 15 litres for the complete journey, hence 60 km travelled in $2\frac{1}{2}$ hours. This is 12 km for each half hour or 24 km per hour.
- From the graph 6 litres are used each hour, hence 24 km travelled in each hour.

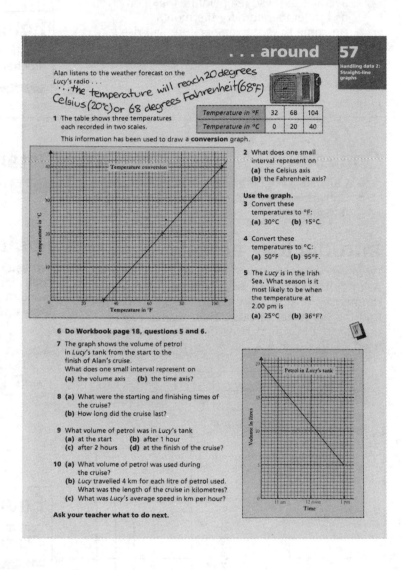

. . . around 57

Handling data 2: Straight-line graphs

Alan listens to the weather forecast on the Lucy's radio . . .

. . .the temperature will reach 20 degrees Celsius (20°C) or 68 degrees Fahrenheit (68°F)

1 The table shows three temperatures each recorded in two scales.

Temperature in °F	32	68	104
Temperature in °C	0	20	40

This information has been used to draw a **conversion** graph.

2 What does one small interval represent on
(a) the Celsius axis
(b) the Fahrenheit axis?

Use the graph.
3 Convert these temperatures to °F:
(a) 30°C (b) 15°C.

4 Convert these temperatures to °C:
(a) 50°F (b) 95°F.

5 The *Lucy* is in the Irish Sea. What season is it most likely to be when the temperature at 2.00 pm is
(a) 25°C (b) 36°F?

6 **Do Workbook page 18, questions 5 and 6.**

7 The graph shows the volume of petrol in *Lucy's* tank from the start to the finish of Alan's cruise.
What does one small interval represent on
(a) the volume axis   (b) the time axis?

8 (a) What were the starting and finishing times of the cruise?
(b) How long did the cruise last?

9 What volume of petrol was in *Lucy's* tank
(a) at the start   (b) after 1 hour
(c) after 2 hours   (d) at the finish of the cruise?

10 (a) What volume of petrol was used during the cruise?
(b) *Lucy* travelled 4 km for each litre of petrol used. What was the length of the cruise in kilometres?
(c) What was *Lucy's* average speed in km per hour?

Ask your teacher what to do next.

S30
Handling
data 2:
Trend graphs

HD2cf/4

D/E1
I/D1
I/E2

Content

- Interpretation and construction of trend graphs.

Introductory activity

Travel brochures
Provide a selection of travel brochures containing details of the weather at various holiday places, for example: temperatures, hours of sunshine, number of rainy days. In some brochures this information may be presented as bar or bar-line graphs. Discuss in particular the 'monthly temperatures' data:

- the highest temperature reached each day might be recorded for the month and the average of these temperatures is often given as the temperature for the month
- on some days the temperature will rise above this average, on others it will not – draw a specific example from the brochure.

Detailed notes

Q2c The completed graph is 'U' shaped (the temperature falls in the first half of the year, is at its lowest in the middle (July) and rises towards the end of the year).

Additional activity

Comparing seasons
The two finished graphs can be contrasted. Discussion could centre around the seasons. For example, when is summer in England, when is summer in Australia? Which country has colder winters, hotter summers?

Equipment

For the Introductory activity: travel company brochures containing weather information.

S31
Handling
data 2:
Straight-line
graphs

A2c/5
HD2cf/5

O/C2
D/E1

Content

- Calculation of perimeters of regular shapes
- Construction and interpretation of straight-line graphs.

Introductory activity

Perimeter of a rhombus
Ask pupils to draw on 1 cm isometric dot paper rhombuses of side 1 cm, 2 cm, . . . 5 cm and then find the perimeter of each. Their results can be discussed and summarised in a table and then used to draw graph A.

Length of side in cm	1	2	3	4	5
Perimeter in cm	4	8	12	16	20

Rhombuses

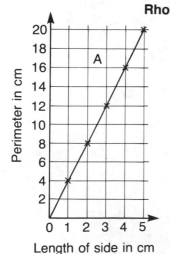
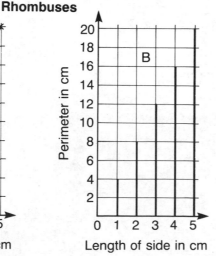

Highlight that

- axes should be labelled
- the graph should be titled
- the plotted points lie on a straight line.

It might be useful to use the results to draw graph B first and highlight the points listed in the Introductory activity for Core Textbook page 56.

Detailed notes

Q3b $\frac{1}{2}$ cm squared paper is suitable for this graph.

Additional activity

Perimeter of rectangles of equal breadth
Pupils could construct another straight-line graph based on drawing this sequence of rectangles on 1 cm squared paper.

Equipment

$\frac{1}{2}$ cm and 1 cm squared paper, 1 cm isometric dot paper, ruler.

S32
Handling data 2: Straight-line graphs

A2c/5
HD2cf/5

O/C2
D/E1
I/D1

Content

- Calculation of distance given speed and time
- Interpretation and construction of straight-line graphs.

Introductory activity

Graphs for 'steady speed'

Describe *The Sun Seeker*, a solar powered car which travels at a steady speed of 8 km per hour during a four hour trial. Ask pupils to complete a time/distance table for the car.

Time in hours	1	2	3	4
Distance in km	8			

Construct a straight-line graph and help pupils to interpret it.
- How far had the *The Sun Seeker* travelled in 2 hours, $\frac{1}{2}$ h, $3\frac{1}{2}$ h?
- How long did it take to travel 24 km, 20 km?

Language such as time axis, distance axis should be used.

Equipment

Ruler.

E13
Handling data 2: Curved-line graphs

A2c/5
HD2cf/5

D/E1
I/D1

Content

- Interpretation and construction of curved-line graphs.

Introductory activity

Sailing at a changing rate

Group discussion: In any clockwork toy, as the spring unwinds, the movement of the toy becomes slower until it eventually stops. Because the motor boat *Kitty* is slowing down, it does *not* cover equal distances in equal times. By studying the graph, pupils will note that during the first 20 seconds of *Kitty*'s journey it travelled 9 metres, whereas in the next 20 seconds it travelled only 4 metres. The distance/time graph of the journey is therefore a curved line.

Detailed notes

Q5 The boat has travelled the same distance after 80, 90 and 100 seconds because it has stopped. Pupils may suggest that the spring of the clockwork motor has fully unwound.

Q7 The graph of *Kitty*'s journey shows that the total distance travelled is 16 metres. On the plan of the boating pond pupils could measure the length of *Kitty*'s journey using a piece of string and check that it is approximately 16 metres.

Q8 Use 2 mm squared paper and the same scales as for the graph of *Kitty*'s journey. The points should be joined with as smooth a curve as possible.

Additional Activity

Temperature of cooling water

The following workcard could be used to give pupils another opportunity of drawing a curved-line graph of a 'different' shape.

Use 2mm squared paper.

Water was boiled and allowed to cool. The temperature of the water after various times is shown in the table.

Time in minutes	0	10	20	30	40	50	60	70	80
Temperature in °C	100	60	40	30	24	22	20	20	20

1 Use the information in the table to draw a curved-line graph.
2 Why did the temperature of the water not fall below 20°C?

Equipment

2 mm squared paper, string or thread.

E14

Handling
data 2:
Travel graphs

HD2cf/5

D/E1
I/D1

Content

- Interpretation and construction of travel graphs.

The term *travel graph* is used for line graphs which show how much of a journey has been completed with the passing of time.

Introductory activity

Graph of a car's journey

The idea of a 'travel' graph could be introduced by drawing the simple graph of a car's journey shown below.

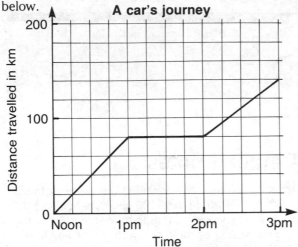

The first sloping line indicates that from noon to 1 pm the car has travelled at a constant speed (average of 80 km/h). From 1 pm to 2 pm the line is horizontal indicating that no distance has been covered, that is, the car has stopped. The second sloping line indicates that from 2pm to 3pm the car has travelled on, again at a constant speed (average of 60 km/h).

Detailed notes

Graph The thicker vertical lines for each hour interval make it easier for pupils to interpret times on the graph. The labels 'Leave Oran', etc. should also help.

Q6 Use $\frac{1}{2}$ cm squared paper and the same scales as for the graph of *Seamist*'s cruise.

Additional activity

Linking speed and the slope of the graph

The pupils could calculate the average speed for each part of *Seamist*'s journey. For example:

Time from Oran to Rona– 1 hour
Distance– 20 km
Speed– 20 km per hour.

Help may be required in finding the average speed between Kerry and Oran. Pupils could be asked if they notice any relationship between the slopes of the different parts of the graph and the average speeds over the corresponding parts.

Equipment

$\frac{1}{2}$ cm squared paper, ruler.

E15

Handling
data 2:
Straight-line
graphs

A2c/6 → 7
HD2cf/6

D/E1
I/D1

Content

- Interpretation and construction of straight-line graphs.

Two straight-line graphs appear in the same diagram.

Detailed notes

Q2 'If you want to choose the cheaper hire then for hires lasting
- less than 6 hours, use Suresail
- more than 6 hours, use Marina Craft
- 6 hours, use either as both firms charge the same.'

Q3b Pupils should choose the size of squared paper. Possible scales for 2 mm paper are 1 small interval represents £1 and 6 min (or 12 min) on the respective axes.
For $\frac{1}{2}$ cm paper 1 small interval might represent £2 and 15 min (or 30 min) respectively.

Q4b 'If you want to choose the cheaper hire then for hires lasting
- less than 4 hours, use Suresail
- more than 4 hours, use Marina Craft
- 4 hours, use either as both firms charge the same.'

Additional activity

Choosing the hire company

Ask pupils to suggest reasons why someone might not want to choose the hire company which charges less. For example, the dearer company might have newer or more powerful boats or boats that can carry more passengers and so on.

Equipment

2 mm or $\frac{1}{2}$ cm squared paper, ruler.

DETOURS IN PART 2

General advice about using the Detours can be found on page T6 of these notes.

Content

- Meaning and use of inequality symbols
  $<$, $>$
- Interpretation of a decision-tree diagram.

Organisation

Pupils could discuss the questions in pairs.

Equipment

None.

45
Detour:
Equalities and
inequalities

UA3ab/5
N2a/4

FE/D1

Detailed notes

Panels above Q1
To help pupils distinguish between $<$ and $>$ these symbols can be thought of as being derived from the equals symbol by closing its ends – the 'wide' end is next to the larger number and the narrow end is next to the smaller number.

Q1
Two pupils could read alternate examples to each other rather than write each answer in words.

Q2,3
Answers could be written on slips of paper or card and retained for future oral practice.

Q4
Pupils could write each number on a different piece of paper and then follow along the paths of the decision tree. Before writing the prize list the final position of the numbers could be compared with that of a partner.

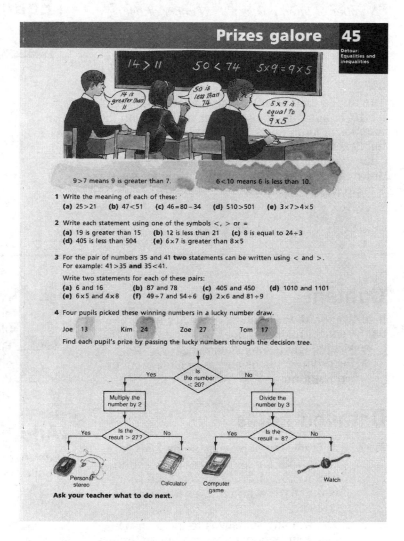

Prizes galore 45

14 > 11   50 < 74   5 × 9 = 9 × 5

14 is greater than 11

50 is less than 74

5 × 9 is equal to 9 × 5

9 > 7 means 9 is greater than 7.   6 < 10 means 6 is less than 10.

1 Write the meaning of each of these:
(a) 25 > 21   (b) 47 < 51   (c) 46 = 80 − 34   (d) 510 > 501   (e) 3 × 7 > 4 × 5

2 Write each statement using one of the symbols $<$, $>$ or =
(a) 19 is greater than 15   (b) 12 is less than 21   (c) 8 is equal to 24 ÷ 3
(d) 405 is less than 504   (e) 6 × 7 is greater than 8 × 5

3 For the pair of numbers 35 and 41 **two** statements can be written using $<$ and $>$.
For example: 41 > 35 **and** 35 < 41.

Write two statements for each of these pairs:
(a) 6 and 16   (b) 87 and 78   (c) 405 and 450   (d) 1010 and 1101
(e) 6 × 5 and 4 × 8   (f) 49 ÷ 7 and 54 ÷ 6   (g) 2 × 6 and 81 ÷ 9

4 Four pupils picked these winning numbers in a lucky number draw.

Joe 13   Kim 24   Zoe 27   Tom 17

Find each pupil's prize by passing the lucky numbers through the decision tree.

Is the number < 20?
— Yes → Multiply the number by 2
— No → Divide the number by 3

Multiply the number by 2 → Is the result > 27?
— Yes → Personal stereo
— No → Calculator

Divide the number by 3 → Is the result = 8?
— Yes → Computer game
— No → Watch

Ask your teacher what to do next.

54
W17
Detour:
Word
formulae

A3b/5

FE/D1

Content

- Recognition of the relationship between two sets of numbers
- Expression of this relationship in words (a word formula).

Introductory activity

Lamp posts and lights
The scene could be set by introducing this problem to the pupils. Each lamp post on the Westfield Estate has three lights.

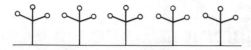

Ask the pupils to draw and complete the table below.

Number of lamp posts	Number of lights
2 →	6
3 →	
4 →	
5 →	

The pupils then have to state a relationship *in words* relating the total number of lights with the number of lamp posts, that is 'the number of lights is three times the number of lamp posts'. This 'word formula' can then be verified by drawing to check the number of lights for say 6 or 8 lamp posts.

Detailed notes

W17, Q1a, 2a, 3a Pupils should draw the next two in the sequence in the space provided. The first five entries in the table can be completed before pupils look for the relationship which is used to predict the entries in the remaining boxes.

Additional activity

Lamp posts and flower beds
On part of Westfield Estate, there are two flower beds between each pair of lamp posts. Ask pupils how to find the number of flower beds when the number of lamp posts is known (multiply by 2 then subtract 2).

Equipment

None.

Content

Investigation of the winning strategies in a mathematical number game.

- Making and testing statements
- Recording findings and presenting them in written form.

Detailed notes

Rules Another way of playing Target Zero is to begin with a pile of 10 counters and in turn remove 1 or 2 counters. The winner is the player who removes the last counter(s).

Q1b The winning strategy is to try to ensure that your opponent has to subtract from a multiple of 3. For example, if your opponent has to subtract from 9 then either 8 or 7 is left. You can then subtract 2 or 1 leaving 6. This is repeated to leave 3, then again to leave zero.

Q2b The first player can always win since these numbers are not multiples of 3.

Q2c Pupils may discover that if the starting number is any multiple of 3 then the first player cannot be sure of winning.

Q3b Pupils need to ensure that their opponent always has to subtract from a multiple of 4.

Q4 Pupils are likely to suggest that each player can subtract 1 *or* 2 *or* 3 *or* 4.

Additional activity

Reach zero to lose
Pupils could investigate a strategy for a version of this game in which the *loser* subtracts to leave zero.

Equipment

Counters may be useful.

Content

- Construction of a bar graph
- Identification of sets of numbers including even and odd.

Problem-solving procedures are used in the interpretation of letters and numbers on car number plates.

Organisation

Pupils could discuss the questions in pairs.

Introductory activity

Looking at number plates

Pupils could be asked to note down and then look at a selection of car number plates. Through discussion they should realise that the letters and numbers provide data about the place and time of registration of the car. The meaning of registration should be clarified.

Detailed notes

Q1c The coloured bars of the graph should be spaced out as shown.

Q2 One pupil could note the number plates of ten cars in the school car park or you could ask pupils to note ten on their way from and to school.

Q3 This should be set as a *Challenge*. Adults at home could be asked to help.

Equipment

Coloured pencils.

UA3d/3
N3a/3 → 4
HD2c/3

PSE
I/E1

E17	E18, E19	E20	E21	E22
The School Concert	How many seats in the hall?	Programme planning	The Concert Kiosk	Guess the weight

CONTENT AND DEVELOPMENT

Throughout Heinemann Mathematics mathematical ideas are presented in contexts designed to show a variety of real-life situations in which mathematics is useful. Some of these contexts have been extended to occupy a whole section.

General advice concerning the purpose of and management of an 'extended context' can be found on page T6 of these notes.

In this extension section the context of a School Concert is based on the fictitious Gladeside School. Some of the activities could be used as a basis for developing work for pupils in their own school. Activities revolve around discussing fund raising ideas, investigating the school hall seating arrangements, planning the concert programme, raising funds, spending the profits.

The contents include:

- discussion
- report writing
- art/craft – design of a programme leaflet and ticket
- practical measurement of length and volume
- estimation of weight
- interpretation and construction of scale drawing
- whole number and money calculations including simple percentages
- calculation of profit
- problem solving
  - interpretation of information presented in written, tabular and visual form
  - presentation of findings in written and visual form
  - methodical working
  - elimination, reasoning, trial and improvement strategies.

National Curriculum (England and Wales)

UA1ab, 2abc, 3cd
N3c, 4ab
SM3d

Mathematics 5–14 (Scotland)

PSE
AS/D2, D3, E3,
MD/D4
RN/E1
FPR/E2
ME/D, D1, D6, D8
PFS/E3
T/D2

EQUIPMENT

An enlarged version of the profits table, calculator, chairs, metre stick or tape, 1 cm squared paper, ruler, material on which to design a programme and ticket for the concert, plastic cup, 2 litre bottle, a parcel or tin filled with sand, a set of weighing scales.

Content

- Presentation of findings in written form
- Interpretation of written information.

Introductory activity

Setting the scene
Introduce the fictitious Gladeside School and explain its need to raise funds to purchase additional resources. Examples of such resources, selected from Page 72 of the Goodies Catalogue, are illustrated on the page.
Staff and pupils at Gladeside have decided to raise money by organising a school concert. Focus pupils' attention on things which would make such a concert a success, for example: making a profit, decorating the hall or theatre, advertising, and so on.

Six suggestions are provided on the page to help initiate discussion, pupils should be encouraged to think of other ideas and preferably to express them in a form extended beyond a single sentence. The discussion should enhance the scene setting for the activities which lie ahead.

Equipment

An enlarged version of the profits table in Q2 could be prepared and displayed to focus pupils' attention on the development of the context.

E17
Extended
Context:
The School
Concert

UA1ab/4

PSE

Content

- Measurement to the nearest centimetre and to the nearest metre
- Interpretation and application of a scale
- Interpretation and construction of a scale diagram
- Calculations involving simple percentages, addition and multiplication of money
- Conversion of units (metres/centimetres)
- Problem solving: methodical working, reasoning
- Interpretation of a calculator display in context
- Presentation of findings in written and visual form.

Detailed notes

Q1 Space to arrange chairs will be needed. Two rows of three chairs should be used in determining the distances. Discuss the meaning of being seated comfortably and the factors which affect the distance between rows. For example, leg room for an adult, people moving along the row to reach their seat and so on.

Q3b The term 'passage' may be unfamiliar to some pupils.

Page 19, plan Each seating area at Gladeside is 16 m by 7 m.

Q4 Discussion should establish that the feet of the people in the first row should not extend into the passage, that is the back of the chairs of the first row should be 1 metre from the front boundary.

Q6, last line The amount could be recorded on the enlarged profits table on display.

Q7 Some pupils may have difficulty in deciding the position of the centre passage. Discuss the idea of a line of symmetry. Note that some halls may not lend themselves to a centre passage.

Q8b Since this involves the use of practical measurements obtained by the pupils it is anticipated that some interpretation of a calculator display resulting from the division calculations may be required.

Q7,8 Encourage pupils to write an account of their findings. A display of the resulting plans showing the rows of seats in position could be made.

E18
E19
Extended
Context: How
many seats in
the hall?

UA2b, 3c/5
N3c/5
SM3d/6

PSE
FPR/E2
ME/D1
PFS/E3

Equipment

Calculator, chairs, metre stick or tape, 1 cm squared paper, ruler.

E20
Extended
Context:
Programme
planning

UA2ac,
3d/5

PSE
T/D2

Content

- Interpretation of written information and tables
- Time calculations
- Problem solving: elimination, methodical working, reasoning, trial and improvement
- Presentation of findings in written and visual form.

Detailed notes

Intro-duction Before pupils start work on this page, discuss the constraints in planning a concert programme, for example: length of concert item, variety of type of item, performers not being in two consecutive items, time being allowed between items (for applause, performers getting on and off stage, setting the scenery, announcing items and so on).

Q2 Pupils could write each item on a separate strip of paper. The strips could then be moved around to form trial arrangements. Many solutions are possible. To aid checking encourage pupils to mark musical items with a * for easy identification. Other features to look for when checking answers are:
- the first four items are performed by Classes 1 and 2
- the finishing time is 8.06 pm.

Q3a The amount could be recorded on the enlarged profits table on display.

Q3b A display of the designs could be made.

Equipment

Material on which to design a programme and ticket for the concert, calculator.

E21
Extended
Context:
The Concert
Kiosk

N4ab/
5 → 6

PSE
MD/D4
RN/E1
ME/D

Content

- Interpretation of written information
- Practical work involving approximate measurement
- Calculations involving the four operations on money.

Detailed notes

Q5 Answers will vary depending on the size of cup used. Discuss how full the cup should be.

Q8 The amount could be recorded on the enlarged profits table on display.

Additional activities

1 Survey
Discuss with the pupils whether the items chosen for the kiosk by Gladeside pupils would suit their class. Pupils could then conduct a survey to find the most popular items and investigate suitable selling prices.

2 Investigating cups
Pupils could investigate the possibility of selling two different sizes of cups of orange at the kiosk and how that would affect the profits.

Equipment

Plastic cup, 2 litre bottle; calculator.

E22
Extended
Context:
Guess the
weight

UA2c/6
N4ab/6

PSE
AS/D2, D3,
E3
MD/D4
ME/D6, D8

Content

- Interpretation of written information
- Relationship between the kilogram and the gram
- Addition, subtraction and multiplication calculations with whole numbers and money
- Interpretation of a calculator display in context
- Estimation of weight
- Problem solving: methodical working, reasoning, elimination, trial and improvement
- Presentation of findings in written form.

Detailed notes

Q1c Some pupils may have difficulty in appreciating the range of guesses for which the money was returned (1120 g to 1320 g).

Q1d, 3c The amount could be recorded on the enlarged profits table on display.

Q2 Choose a suitable weight of parcel for estimation. A box filled with sand or commercial weights could be parcelled. The parcel could then be weighed and pupils' estimates compared. A record of pupils' estimates should be displayed to highlight the variations likely to occur.

Q3 Calculator displays will need to be interpreted in context. The key ingredient is the chocolate.

Q4 Encourage pupils to discuss the various possibilities and to write a report giving a clear reason for their final choice of items.

Equipment

Calculator, a parcel or tin filled with sand of suitable weight for estimation in Q2, a set of scales to weigh the parcel or tin.

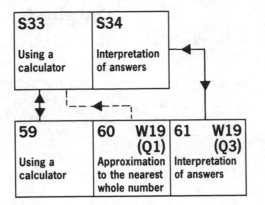

CONTENT AND DEVELOPMENT

Core

Division 1 (on pages 55–59 of these notes) covered work on division of whole numbers by 2 to 10, division of one- and two-place decimals by 2 to 10, the unitary method of proportion.

Division 2 extends the work on whole number division using the calculator and approximation and interpretation of the answer to a division problem. It covers:

- division by a two-digit whole number using the calculator
- approximation to the nearest whole number
- interpretation of an answer to a division problem in context
- calculation of exact remainders.

Decimals 3 (on pages 91–96 of these notes) covers work on division of decimals and approximation to the first decimal place.

Support

This material provides alternative or additional work to that in the core and also contains some work on the division of decimals.

National Curriculum (England and Wales)

N3bce, 4bd
HD2ad

Mathematics 5–14 (Scotland)

I/D1
RTN/C1, C3, D1, D4
AS/C4, D3
MD/D4, E4
RN/D1
E+

EQUIPMENT

Calculator, worksheet of blank number lines. For the Introductory activities: centimetre cubes.

59
Division 2:
Using a
calculator

N3bce,
4b/5

RTN/D1, D4
MD/E4

Content

- Division of whole numbers and money by two-digit whole numbers using a calculator
- Calculation of an average
- Relationship between the kilogram and the gram.

Detailed notes

Panel above Q1	Ensure pupils know how to use a calculator for division.
Q5	The weight of the cartons should be converted to grams.
Q7	Ensure pupils can interpret a calculator answer in the context of money, that is 2·4 is written as £2·40 and 0·07 as £0·07 or 7 pence.

Equipment

Calculator.

60
W19
(Q1)
Division 2:
Approxi-
mation to the
nearest whole
number

N4d/5 → 6
HD2ad/
5 → 6

RTN/D1, D4
RN/D1
E+

Content

- Interpretation of tables
- Interpretation and completion of scales marked in tenths
- Calculation of an average
- Division of whole numbers by a two-digit whole number using a calculator
- Approximation of a calculator display to the nearest whole number
- Investigation: survey of class.

Introductory activity

Approximation to the nearest whole number
Draw a blank number line. Demonstrate how to round a calculator display to the nearest whole number, for example:

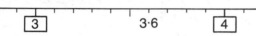

$128 \div 35 = 3{\cdot}6571428$
which lies between 3 and 4.
Put the numbers 3 and 4 in the boxes.

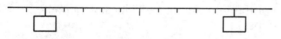

Count up from 3·1 to 3·6.

Establish by discussion that 3·6571428 is '3·6 and a bit', and use an arrow to indicate its approximate position on the number line.

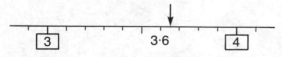

Show the position of 3·6571428 relative to each box, indicating that it is nearer 4.
So 3·6571428 is *4 to the nearest whole number*.

This activity should be repeated for several examples. Some suggestions are: $341 \div 30$, $90 \div 17$, $245 \div 19$.

Detailed notes

| Panel above Q1 | Ensure pupils know that mean and average are synonymous. |
| W19,Q1 | Pupils should complete the number lines as well as the calculations. |

Additional activity

Class averages
Pupils could find, to the nearest whole number, the mean weight, height, handspan, etc. of their class or year group.

Equipment

Calculator, a worksheet of blank number lines may be helpful to some pupils.

Content

- Interpretation of written information and tables
- Division of whole numbers by two-digit whole numbers using a calculator
- Interpretation of a decimal calculator display in context
- Calculation of exact remainders.

Introductory activity

Calculating exact remainders
The interpretation of a calculator display following a division, and the calculation of the remainder, may be explained in a practical way, for example: Choc bars are to be packaged in threes. How many packs can be made from 17 choc bars and how many are left over?

Use centimetre cubes to find the answer in a practical way.

□□□ □□□ □□□ □□□ □□□   □ □
5 packs   2 left over

Now use a calculator
$17 \div 3 = 5{\cdot}6666666$
This means that there are 5 packs and 'a bit'.
5 packs hold $5 \times 3 = 15$ choc bars
There are $17 - 15 = 2$ choc bars left.

Repeat this activity for several more examples, gradually introducing larger numbers where a model is impractical.

Equipment

Calculator.
For Introductory activity: centimetre cubes.

Detailed notes

Panel above Q1	Discuss the example with the pupils ensuring that they understand the context used.
Q2c	Interpretation may cause difficulty. The number of boxes that have to be opened is one more than the number of full boxes used.
W19,Q3	Ensure pupils understand the layout of the answers.

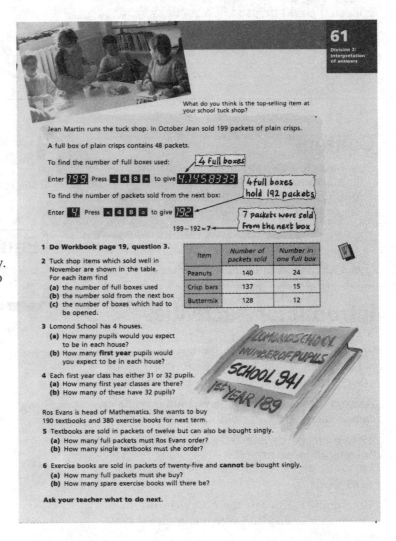

61
Division 2:
Interpretation
of answers

What do you think is the top-selling item at your school tuck shop?

Jean Martin runs the tuck shop. In October Jean sold 199 packets of plain crisps.

A full box of plain crisps contains 48 packets.

To find the number of full boxes used: *4 full boxes*

Enter **199** Press **÷ 4 8 =** to give **4.1458333**   *4 full boxes hold 192 packets*

To find the number of packets sold from the next box:

Enter **4** Press **× 4 8 =** to give **192**   *7 packets were sold from the next box*

$199 - 192 = 7$

1 **Do Workbook page 19, question 3.**

2 Tuck shop items which sold well in November are shown in the table. For each item find
(a) the number of full boxes used
(b) the number sold from the next box
(c) the number of boxes which had to be opened.

Item	Number of packets sold	Number in one full box
Peanuts	140	24
Crisp bars	137	15
Buttermix	128	12

3 Lomond School has 4 houses.
(a) How many pupils would you expect to be in each house?
(b) How many **first year** pupils would you expect to be in each house?

4 Each first year class has either 31 or 32 pupils.
(a) How many first year classes are there?
(b) How many of these have 32 pupils?

LOMOND SCHOOL NUMBER OF PUPILS
SCHOOL 941
1ST YEAR 189

Ros Evans is head of Mathematics. She wants to buy 190 textbooks and 380 exercise books for next term.

5 Textbooks are sold in packets of twelve but can also be bought singly.
(a) How many full packets must Ros Evans order?
(b) How many single textbooks must she order?

6 Exercise books are sold in packets of twenty-five and **cannot** be bought singly.
(a) How many full packets must she buy?
(b) How many spare exercise books will there be?

Ask your teacher what to do next.

S33
Division 2:
Using a
calculator

N3e, 4b/5

I/D1
RTN/C3
AS/D3
MD/D4

Content

- Interpretation of tables and diagrams
- Calculator division of two-digit whole numbers and two-place decimals
- Calculation of an average.

Introductory activity

Weather
If possible arrange a cross-curricular link with the Geography department. Pupils could make a collection of weather maps from newspapers. Discuss the various symbols used in a weather map.

Discuss the various units used to record different aspects of weather, for example:

sunshine – hours
wind speed – miles per hour
rain – centimetres
temperature – degrees Celsius.

Some pupils may need to be shown how to calculate an average. Real data which pupils have collected could be used in a similar way to the examples on the page. Averages should be taken over 5 days to avoid non-terminating decimals.

Detailed notes

Q1 It may be helpful for pupils to list the windspeeds and the temperatures before finding the totals.

Q2d Some pupils may need to be reminded that there are 30 days in June.

Q3, graph The broken vertical axes may need to be explained.

Equipment

Calculator.

S34
Division 2:
Interpretation
of answers

N3e, 4b/5

RTN/C1
AS/C4
MD/D4
RN/D1

Content

- Interpretation of written information, diagrams and tables
- Division of two-, three- and four-digit whole numbers by a two-digit whole number using a calculator
- Interpretation of a decimal calculator display in context
- Calculation of exact remainders.

Introductory activities

1 Rounding up or down?
Revise the idea that when the answer to a division is not exact, it may have to be rounded up or down depending on the context. For example:

Gemma, the jeweller, displays 140 bracelets on cards. Each card can hold up to 15 bracelets.

'How many cards does she *need* to display all the bracelets?' gives rise to
$140 \div 15 = 9.3333333$ which is rounded *up* to 10 cards.

'How many cards can she *fill*?' gives rise to
$140 \div 15 = 9.3333333$ which is rounded *down* to 9 cards.

2 Calculating exact remainders
Discuss method of recording used in Q3 using the approach described in the Introductory activity for Core Textbook page 61.

Equipment

Calculator.
For Introductory activity 2: centimetre cubes.

CONTENT AND DEVELOPMENT

Core

Previous work on symmetry dealt with shapes having one or more axes of symmetry. The *Shape patterns* section on pages 10–12 of these notes covered work on the circle.

Symmetry covers:

■ concept of rotational symmetry
■ finding how often a shape fits its own outline in one full turn
■ interpretation of codes.

Tessellations (on pages 132–134 of these notes) deals with tiling properties of geometrical and composite shapes.

National Curriculum (England and Wales)

SM2c, 3b

Mathematics 5–14 (Scotland)

PSE
RS/D2, D3
S/E1

RELATED ACTIVITIES

1 Snowflake designs
These could be made using Turtle graphics.

2 Road signs
Use these as a source of shapes. Examine them for rotational and line symmetry.

3 Car and company logos
These can be found in advertisements and magazines and provide another source of environmental shapes.
Pupils could also make displays of examples of shapes which show rotational symmetry.

EQUIPMENT

Tracing paper or thin plain paper, a copy of the *Highway Code*.
For the Introductory activities: squared paper, card, glue, compasses.

62

Symmetry:
Rotating
designs

SM2c, 3b/5

**PSE
S/E1**

Content

- Concept of rotational symmetry
- Identification of rotational symmetry in shapes and shape patterns
- Finding how often a shape fits its own outline in one complete turn.

Introductory activities

1 Fitting twice
- Make a coloured 'flag' like this.

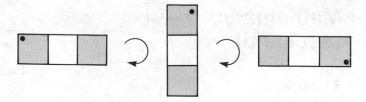

- Mark a corner of the 'flag' with a dot.
- Rotate the flag as shown.
- Discuss with pupils when it 'looks the same'. There are two positions, the starting position and when it has been given a half turn.

2 Fitting three times
- Make a circular design like this. The method is described on Core Textbook page 13.

- Show pupils how to make a tracing of the shape using tracing paper or thin plain paper.
- Colour alternate 'petals' red on the design and the tracing.
- Mark a 'petal' on the tracing with a dot.
- Rotate the tracing and find how often the tracing fits the original design in one full turn.

There are three positions, including the starting position, when the shape fits its outline. Emphasise that the fitting occurs when both shape and colour match.

3 Fitting four times
- On squared paper make a shape like this.

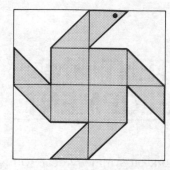

- Stick the shape on cardboard and cut it out.
- Mark a corner of the shape with a dot.
- Hold the shape against the blackboard and draw its outline.
- Rotate the shape to see how often it fits its outline in one full turn (four times).

All the above activities could equally well be demonstrated using an OHP and acetate sheets.

Equipment

Tracing paper or thin plain paper, a copy of the *Highway Code*.
For the Introductory activities: squared paper, card, glue, compasses.

63
W28
Symmetry:
Rotations

SM2c, 3b/5

**RS/D2, D3
S/E1**

Content

- Interpretation of the international code flags
- Identification of rotational symmetry in shapes
- Finding the number of times a geometrical shape fits its outline in one complete turn.

Introductory activity

Detailed notes

Q3 Some pupils may need to trace each flag to check if it is upside down. Turning upside down is not the same as rotating through 180°, for example, flag L.

Q4 There are many possibilities here, but flags L, N and U are probably the most difficult ones to spot.

INTERNATIONAL CODE OF SIGNALS

A	Diver down – keep well clear.	N	No (negative).
B	Discharging or carrying dangerous goods.	O	Man overboard.
C	Yes (affirmative).	P	(At sea) – nets fast on obstruction.
D	Keep clear – manoeuvring with difficulty.	Q	I request free pratique.
E	Altering my course to starboard.	R	
F	I am disabled – communicate.	S	My engines going astern.
G	I require a pilot (I am hauling nets)	T	Keep clear – pair trawling.
H	Pilot on board.	U	You are running into danger.
I	Altering my course to port.	V	I require assistance.
J	On fire – dangerous cargo, keep well clear.	W	I require medical assistance.
K	Communicate with me.	X	Stop and await my signals.
L	Stop your vessel instantly.	Y	I am dragging my anchor.
M	My vessel is stopped.	Z	I require a tug

International code of signals

These flags can be used by sailors as a means of communicating from ship to ship, or ship to shore. The individual letter flags have special meanings as shown here. There are also flags for the digits 0 to 9.

With improved radio communications flags are less significant than they used to be. However some of the flags are used regularly in yacht and dinghy racing and other special meanings are assigned to them for this purpose. Discuss the flags with the pupils.

Additional activities

1 Line symmetry

Pupils could investigate the line symmetry of the flags.

2 Making flags

A group of pupils could make a set of coloured code flags. This would entail some accurate measurement work, careful drawing and colouring. The finished flags could be displayed.

Equipment

Tracing paper may be required for some pupils.

FRACTIONS 2

64	65	66	67
Whole number times a fraction	Whole number times a mixed number	Fraction of a whole number	Fraction of a whole number

CONTENT AND DEVELOPMENT

Core

Fractions 1 (on pages 48–50 of these notes) was the first section of work on fractions and included equivalence of fractions, expressing one number as a fraction of another and addition and subtraction of halves and quarters.

Fractions 2 contains further work on fractions and covers:

- multiplication of a fraction or mixed number by a whole number
- calculation of a fraction of a whole number.

As far as possible, the work is set in realistic contexts. The examples are fairly simple allowing much of the work to be done mentally.

National Curriculum (England and Wales)

N3ce, 4ab

Mathematics 5–14 (Scotland)

FPR/C, D1, E2
E+

EQUIPMENT

Calculator.
For an Introductory activity: squared paper, coloured pencils.

Content

- Multiplication of a fraction by a whole number.

Introductory activities

1 The meaning of $3 \times \frac{1}{4}$
Discuss with the pupils the fact that $2 + 2 + 2$ is 3 lots of 2 and can be written as 3×2. Refer to the illustrative panel. In the same way the amount of pizza eaten altogether is $\frac{1}{4} + \frac{1}{4} + \frac{1}{4}$ or 3 lots of $\frac{1}{4}$ which can be written as $3 \times \frac{1}{4}$.

- Pupils could be asked to write the multiplication statements for particular scenarios, for example 'Find the total weight of 2 parcels each weighing $\frac{4}{10}$ kg' or to write multiplication statements for given shaded fractional diagrams:

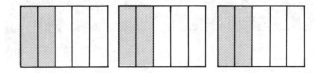

Total amount shaded is $3 \times \frac{2}{5}$

- Pupils should also be asked to draw diagrams to represent multiplication statements such as $4 \times \frac{3}{8}, 3 \times \frac{3}{4}$

2 Calculation of $3 \times \frac{1}{4}$
The answer to $3 \times \frac{1}{4}$ can be found by verbalising the multiplication statement.

$$3 \times \frac{1}{4} = \frac{3}{4}$$

> 3 times 1 quarter is 3 quarters.

By doing several examples in this way pupils should realise that when multiplying a fraction by a whole number, the *numerator only* of the fraction is multiplied.

Detailed notes

Q1 Answers are less than 1.
Q2 Answers are whole numbers.
Q3 Answers are improper fractions which have to be expressed as mixed numbers.

Equipment

None.

Fractions 2: Whole number times a fraction

N3c, 4a/5

E+

Content

- Multiplication of a mixed number by a whole number.

Introductory activity

Using the Distributive Law
Remind pupils of a mental method of multiplying, for example, 3×54 using the Distributive Law.

> 3×54 is
> 3 lots of 50 and 3 lots of 4
> which is 150 and 12.
> This gives a total of 162.

This method can be used to multiply a mixed number by a whole number by first multiplying the whole number part, then the fractional part and adding the answers.

Discuss the method used to find the answer for each example in the panels.

Detailed notes

Q1,2,3 The multiplication of the fractional part results in a simple fraction or a whole number and hence the answers can be found mentally.
Q4,5 The multiplication of the fractional part results in an improper fraction. With these more difficult examples, pupils may need to use a systematic form of recording as suggested in the panel above Q4.

Equipment

None.

65
Fractions 2: Whole number times a mixed number

N3c, 4ab/5

E+

Content

- Calculation of a fraction of a whole number (and application to money and measures).

Introductory activity

Finding $\frac{1}{4}$ of, $\frac{1}{5}$ of ... by division
Some pupils may have to be reminded of the equivalence of a 'fractional part' of a number and division, for example, the equivalence of $\frac{1}{4}$ of 16 and $16 \div 4$.

Use a piece of squared paper made up of 16 smaller squares. Fold the paper into quarters and colour one quarter to show that $\frac{1}{4}$ of 16 squares is 4 squares, that is $\frac{1}{4}$ of $16 = 4$.

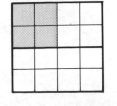

But 16 squares shared among 4 gives 4, that is $16 \div 4 = 4$.

$\frac{1}{4}$ of 16 is the same as $16 \div 4$

Detailed notes

Q4 It may be necessary to explain that the unit of measurement should be changed to that shown in brackets. Recording should be as indicated in the worked example beside Q4.

Equipment

Calculator.
For the Introductory activity: squared paper, coloured pencils.

66
Fractions 2: Fraction of a whole number

N3c, 4a/5

FPR/C1, D1, E2

67
Fractions 2:
Fraction of a
whole number

N3ce,
4ab/5

FPR/D1, E2

Content

- Calculation of a fraction of a whole number (and application to money and measure).

Introductory activity

Finding $\frac{3}{4}$ of, $\frac{4}{5}$ of ... by division, then multiplication
Remind pupils of the work on Core Textbook page 64, where they learned through verbalisation that $3 \times \frac{1}{4} = \frac{3}{4}$
Therefore $\frac{3}{4}$ can be considered as $3 \times \frac{1}{4}$ or 3 lots of $\frac{1}{4}$.
Consequently to find $\frac{3}{4}$ of 24,
find $\frac{1}{4}$ of 24 and multiply the answer by 3.

To find $\frac{4}{5}$ of 20,
find $\frac{1}{5}$ of 20 and multiply the answer by 4, and so on.
Give several practice examples involving the same whole number. For example, find $\frac{1}{8}$ of 72.
Now find $\frac{3}{8}$ of 72, $\frac{5}{8}$ of 72, $\frac{7}{8}$ of 72.

Equipment

Calculator.

Detailed notes

Q3 The unit of measurement should be changed to that shown in brackets. Recording should be as in the worked example beside Q3.

Q5 By using the calculator as shown in the worked example beside Q5, the need to write the answer to the 'unitary' fraction first is eliminated.

Panel above Q7 Pupils will require an explanation of the term carat (ct) which is a measure used to indicate the purity of gold. 24ct is pure gold. A measure of 9ct means that 9 parts in 24 parts of the metal or $\frac{9}{24}$ is gold.

Q8 It is likely that, when finding the weight of pure gold ($\frac{9}{24}$ of pupil's weight), the answer will have to be rounded. Some pupils may need help with this.

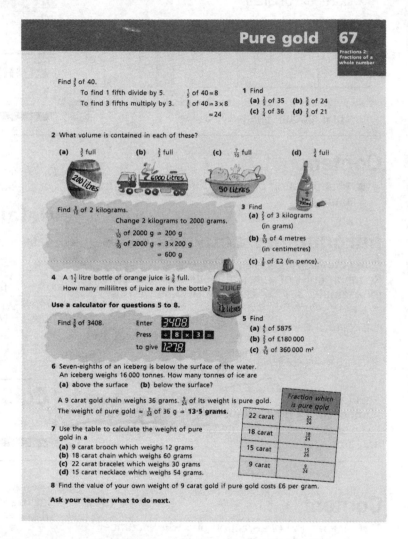

Pure gold **67**

Fractions 2:
Fractions of a
whole number

Find $\frac{3}{5}$ of 40.
To find 1 fifth divide by 5. $\frac{1}{5}$ of 40 = 8
To find 3 fifths multiply by 3. $\frac{3}{5}$ of 40 = 3 × 8
= 24

1 Find
(a) $\frac{2}{5}$ of 35   (b) $\frac{5}{8}$ of 24
(c) $\frac{3}{4}$ of 36   (d) $\frac{2}{3}$ of 21

2 What volume is contained in each of these?
(a) $\frac{3}{4}$ full   (b) $\frac{2}{3}$ full   (c) $\frac{7}{10}$ full   (d) $\frac{3}{4}$ full

Find $\frac{3}{10}$ of 2 kilograms.
Change 2 kilograms to 2000 grams.
$\frac{1}{10}$ of 2000 g = 200 g
$\frac{3}{10}$ of 2000 g = 3 × 200 g
= 600 g

3 Find
(a) $\frac{2}{3}$ of 3 kilograms (in grams)
(b) $\frac{6}{10}$ of 4 metres (in centimetres)
(c) $\frac{3}{4}$ of £2 (in pence).

4 A 1$\frac{1}{2}$ litre bottle of orange juice is $\frac{2}{3}$ full.
How many millilitres of juice are in the bottle?

Use a calculator for questions 5 to 8.

Find $\frac{3}{8}$ of 3408.   Enter 3408
Press ÷ 8 × 3 =
to give 1278

5 Find
(a) $\frac{4}{5}$ of 5875
(b) $\frac{2}{3}$ of £180 000
(c) $\frac{3}{10}$ of 360 000 m²

6 Seven-eighths of an iceberg is below the surface of the water.
An iceberg weighs 16 000 tonnes. How many tonnes of ice are
(a) above the surface   (b) below the surface?

A 9 carat gold chain weighs 36 grams. $\frac{9}{24}$ of its weight is pure gold.
The weight of pure gold = $\frac{9}{24}$ of 36 g = **13·5 grams.**

7 Use the table to calculate the weight of pure gold in a
(a) 9 carat brooch which weighs 12 grams
(b) 18 carat chain which weighs 60 grams
(c) 22 carat bracelet which weighs 30 grams
(d) 15 carat necklace which weighs 54 grams.

	Fraction which is pure gold
22 carat	$\frac{22}{24}$
18 carat	$\frac{18}{24}$
15 carat	$\frac{15}{24}$
9 carat	$\frac{9}{24}$

8 Find the value of your own weight of 9 carat gold if pure gold costs £6 per gram.

Ask your teacher what to do next.

68 W29	69	70	71
Reading scales	Reading to the nearest mark	Cubic centimetres	Cuboids, $V = l \times b \times h$

$\downarrow$

E23
Immersion

CONTENT AND DEVELOPMENT

Core

Previously, pupils should have covered work on: the millilitre and its relationship with the litre, reading scales marked in millilitres and reading to the nearest mark, finding volumes of cuboids made with centimetre cubes by multiplying the volume of one layer by the number of layers, the equivalences of 1000 cm³ to 1 litre and 1 cm³ to 1 ml.

Volume consolidates and extends this work and covers:

- the relationship between the litre, millilitre and cubic centimetre
- reading scales, calibrated in millilitres, to the mark and the nearest mark
- volume of a cuboid, introducing the formula $V = l \times b \times h$.

Extension

E23 contains some work on finding the volumes of objects by immersion in water.

National Curriculum (England and Wales)

SM4abd

Mathematics 5–14 (Scotland)

ME/C6, D3, D6, E1, E6, E7
PFS/E2

RELATED ACTIVITIES

Ask pupils to investigate the relationships between imperial and metric measurements used in capacity:

1 Pints and litres
By filling a measuring jar to the 1 pint mark or a pint milk bottle with water and then measuring the volume of the water in litres, pupils can establish for themselves how many millilitres are in 1 pint.

2 Litres and gallons
By using only a 1 pint milk bottle and a 1 litre measuring jar pupils can find the number of litres in a gallon, given that a gallon is equal to 8 pints.

EQUIPMENT

Cup, mug, containers such as tins and jars, measuring jars including a 1-litre graduated measuring jar, two stones of different sizes and other objects which sink, colouring pencils, elastic band.
For Introductory activities: centimetre cubes.

SM4ab/4

ME/C6, D3,
E1

Content

- The relationship between the litre, millilitre and cubic centimetre
- Reading scales, calibrated in millilitres, to the mark
- Practical measurement.

Introductory activities

1 Millilitres and cubic centimetres
Show the class a 1-litre bottle or measuring jar and remind pupils that
1 litre = 1000 ml = 1000 cm³.

Examine other containers, marked in millilitres or cubic centimetres and ask pupils for an alternative method of expressing each volume.

2 Reading scales to a mark
Pupils could be shown a variety of measuring jars marked with different scales. Enlarged versions of these could be drawn, for example:

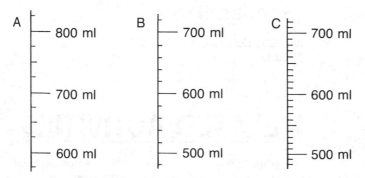

The pupils should be reminded to take certain steps when reading a scale, namely
- find how many small intervals there are between two numbered marks
- determine the volume that is represented by each small interval
- read the volume represented by a specific mark.

Detailed notes

Q6   Pupils may need to be shown how to read the volume correctly. The reading should be taken to the lowest level part of the surface of the liquid as shown.

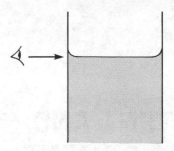

W29,
Q1d   Some pupils may need to be reminded that $\frac{1}{2}$ litre = 500 ml.

Equipment

Cup, mug, measuring jars, colouring pencils. For the Introductory activities: 1-litre bottle or measuring jar.

SM4b/4

ME/C6, D3,
D6, E1, E6

Content

- Reading scales, calibrated in millilitres, to the nearest mark
- Estimation of volumes
- Problem solving – interpretation of written instructions.
- Practical measurement.

Introductory activity

Reading scales to the nearest mark
A scale like the one opposite should be drawn on the blackboard or OHP and discussed to find the approximate volume represented by the pointer. The following steps should be emphasised
- find how many small intervals there are between two numbered marks on the scale (in this case four)
- determine the volume that each small interval represents (25ml in this case)
- state the volumes represented by the other marks
- determine which of these volumes the pointer is nearest (775ml in this case).
Several examples like this should be discussed using different scales.

Detailed notes

Q2   The other containers selected could include a soup bowl, tumbler, tea-pot, and so on.

Q3b   The pupils should first find the volume of the medicine bottle.

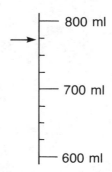

Equipment

Cup, mug, measuring jar, other containers such as tins, jars, etc.

70
Volume:
Cubic
centimetres

SM4d/4

ME/D3
PFS/E2

Content

- Volume of a cuboid as number of centimetre cubes in one layer multiplied by the number of layers.

Introductory activity

Volume of a slab
Discussion should focus on finding the volume of a slab. For example, the slab shown here is made up of 3 rows of cubes.

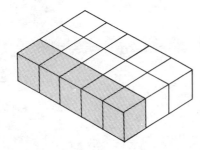

Each row has a volume of 5 cm³, so the volume of the slab is 3 times 5 cm³ = 15 cm³

Some other slabs could be made and the volume of each expressed as a product, for example:

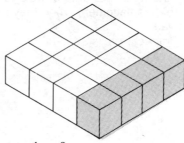

Volume of 1 row = 4 cm³
Number of rows = 4
Volume of slab = 4 × 4 cm³
= 16 cm³

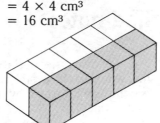

Volume of 1 row = 5 cm³
Number of rows = 2
Volume of slab = 2 × 5 cm³
= 10 cm³

Equipment

For the Introductory activity: centimetre cubes may be useful.

71
Volume:
V - l × b × h

SM4d/
5 → 6

ME/D3
PFS/E2

Content

- Volume of a cuboid using the formula
$V = l \times b \times h$

Introductory activity

The formula $V = l \times b \times h$
Discussion should take place about finding the volume of a cuboid composed of more than one slab.

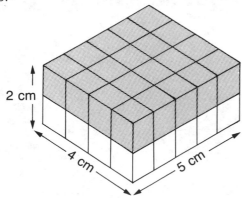

In this cuboid, each slab or layer has 5 cubes in a row and 4 of these rows so the slab has a volume of 5 × 4 cm³. There are two layers so the volume of the whole cuboid is (5 × 4) × 2 cm³ or 5 × 4 × 2 cm³.

Cuboids of different dimensions could then be assembled and pupils asked to say how the volume is found in each one. Pupils should realise that the volume of a cuboid can be found by multiplying together the number of cubes in its length, breadth and height so that $V = l \times b \times h$

Equipment

For the Introductory activity: centimetre cubes may be useful.

E23
Immersion
Volume:
$V = l \times b \times h$

SM4b/4;
4d/5 → 6

ME/C6, D3,
E6, E7

Content

- Finding the volume of objects by measuring the displacement when they are immersed in water
- Practical measurement.

Organisation

It is suggested that Q1 and Q2 are carried out by small groups.

Detailed notes

Q1 Through discussion, establish that when an object sinks and is completely covered by water
- the water rises
- the larger the object, the greater the rise in the water level
- the water displaced is equal to the volume of the object.

Panel above Q2 The measurement in millilitres has to be expressed as cubic centimetres.

Q2 Fill the measuring jar to the 500 ml mark and provide objects which will give a reasonable displacement.

Q4b,c These volumes have first to be calculated in cm³ and then expressed in ml.

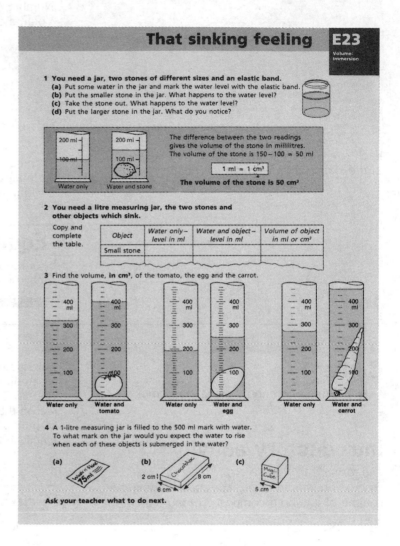

That sinking feeling — E23
Volume: immersion

1 You need a jar, two stones of different sizes and an elastic band.
(a) Put some water in the jar and mark the water level with the elastic band.
(b) Put the smaller stone in the jar. What happens to the water level?
(c) Take the stone out. What happens to the water level?
(d) Put the larger stone in the jar. What do you notice?

The difference between the two readings gives the volume of the stone in millilitres. The volume of the stone is 150 − 100 = 50 ml

$1\text{ ml} = 1\text{ cm}^3$

The volume of the stone is 50 cm³

Water only / Water and stone

2 You need a litre measuring jar, the two stones and other objects which sink.

Copy and complete the table.

Object	Water only – level in ml	Water and object – level in ml	Volume of object in ml or cm³
Small stone			

3 Find the volume, **in cm³**, of the tomato, the egg and the carrot.

Water only / Water and tomato   Water only / Water and egg   Water only / Water and carrot

4 A 1-litre measuring jar is filled to the 500 ml mark with water. To what mark on the jar would you expect the water to rise when each of these objects is submerged in the water?

(a) Wader's Spot 75 ml   (b) Chocolate bar 2 cm / 8 cm / 6 cm   (c) Magic Cube 5 cm

Ask your teacher what to do next.

72	73	74	75	76 W30
The third decimal place, m/mm	The third decimal place, l/ml; kg/g	Place value	Place value using a calculator	Approximation to first decimal place

CONTENT AND DEVELOPMENT

Core

Pupils should be familiar with the relationship between metres/centimetres, litres/millilitres, kilograms/grams.

Decimals 1 (on pages 13–19 of these notes) contained work on place value to hundredths, addition and subtraction, multiplication by 2 to 10 and 100, multiplication by two- and three-digit whole numbers using the calculator.

Decimals 2 (on pages 38–40 of these notes) contained work on conversion between metric and imperial units and decimal work involving length, mass and weight.

Division of decimals is covered in *Division 1* and *2* (on pages 55–59 and 77–80 of these notes).

Decimals 3 extends some of the above work into three-place decimals and introduces rounding to the first decimal place. It covers:

- the introduction of the third decimal place
- conversion of units involving the third decimal place
- addition and subtraction of third-place decimals
- approximation to the first decimal place.

Support

The pupils who have experienced difficulty with *Decimals 1* and *Decimals 2* are not expected to attempt this section. Instead they should continue with the work of *Decimals 1* and *Decimals 2*.

National Curriculum (England and Wales)

N2a, 4d
SM4ab

Mathematics 5–14 (Scotland)

PSE
RTN/E3
AS/D3, E3
MD/E4
RN/E1
ME/E6

RELATED ACTIVITIES

Measurement and the third decimal place
A wall display could be made to demonstrate the uses of the millimetre, millilitre and gram in everyday life. Examples of their use can be found

- in other subject areas, for example, technical subjects, science, home economics
- in items found in shops, for example, bolt sizes, volume of bottles, weight of packets and so on.

EQUIPMENT

Calculator, a worksheet of blank number lines.
For the Introductory activities: a selection of rulers, metre sticks/tapes showing different scale markings, measuring instruments for weight and volume, a selection of packages and containers which display volumes or weights, two sets of digit cards (0 to 9), two cards with a decimal point.
For the calculator games: sets of digit cards, notation cards.

72
Decimals 3:
The third
decimal place,
m/mm

SM4b/4;
4a/5

RTN/E3
ME/E6

Content

- Interpretation of scales
- Place value to thousandths in length
- Relationship between the metre and the millimetre.

Introductory activities

For each activity reference to the scales on the measuring instruments available should be made. Pupils should be encouraged to estimate and then measure objects in the classroom in centimetres and in millimetres. For example:
- height of pupil, desk
- width of desk-top, book, envelope and so on.

1 Revision of second decimal place in length
See Introductory activity 2 for Core Textbook page 15. This could be adapted to relate to length by using a number line to represent part of a metre stick or tape.
Remind pupils that

$$100 \text{ cm} = 1 \text{ m}$$
1 cm is one hundredth of a metre and can be written as 0·01 m

2 Introduction of the third decimal place
A metre stick or tape could be used to compare the relative sizes of different units. Demonstrate that

$$10 \text{ mm} = 1 \text{ cm}$$
$$1 \text{ metre} = 100 \text{ cm} = 100 \times 10 \text{ mm} = 1000 \text{ mm}$$
so 1 mm is 1 thousandth of a metre
and can be written as 0·001 m
70 mm is 70 thousandths of a metre
and can be written as 0·070 m
375 mm is 375 thousandths of a metre
and can be written as 0·375 m.

3 Lengths greater than a metre
Intermediate steps could be used when converting between m and mm and *vice versa*, for example

$$2375 \text{ mm} = 2000 \text{ mm} + 375 \text{ mm}$$
$$= 2 \text{ m} + 375 \text{ mm}$$
$$= 2·375 \text{ m}$$
and also
$$3·125 \text{ m} = 3 \text{ m} + 125 \text{ mm}$$
$$= 3000 \text{ mm} + 125 \text{ mm}$$
$$= 3125 \text{ mm}$$

Care should be taken with examples of the type 1021 mm, 1·005 m
Most pupils should rapidly progress to omitting the intermediate steps.

Equipment

For the Introductory activities: a selection of rulers, metre sticks/tapes showing different scale markings.

Detailed notes

Q2 This marking is common on many metre sticks.

Q3 This marking is more likely to be found on tapes used by tradesmen.

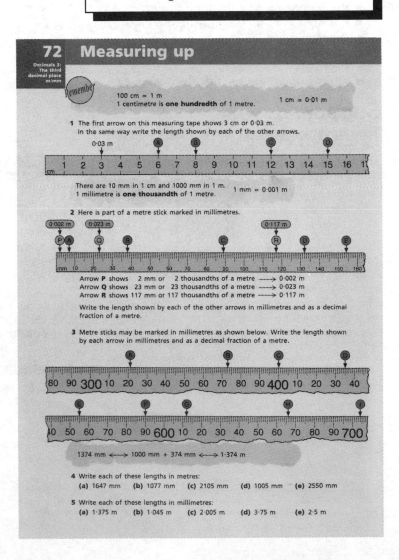

Content

- Place value to thousandths in volume and weight
- Relationship between litres and millilitres, kilograms and grams
- Addition and subtraction of three place decimals.

Introductory activities

In each activity pupils should be encouraged to estimate then measure the volume/weight of suitable containers/packages.

1 The third decimal place in volume
Pupils should be familiar with the relationship

$$1000 \text{ ml} = 1 \text{ litre}.$$
Discuss: 1 ml = 1 thousandth of a litre
$$= 0.001 \text{ litres}$$

Demonstrate relative volumes using different measuring containers and discuss the conversion of millilitres to litres. For example,

1 spoonful =	5 ml =	0.005 l
1 medicine bottle =	75 ml =	0.075 l
1 cupful =	140 ml =	0.140 l
1 milk carton =	1000 ml =	1 l

2 Volumes greater than 1 litre
Use containers with the volume displayed.
Discuss:
$$1750 \text{ ml} = 1000 \text{ ml} + 750 \text{ ml}$$
$$= 1 \text{ l} + 750 \text{ ml}$$
$$= 1.750 \text{ l}$$
and also
$$2.451 \text{ l} = 2 \text{ l} + 451 \text{ ml}$$
$$= 2000 \text{ ml} + 451 \text{ ml}$$
$$= 2451 \text{ ml}$$

The intermediate stages may not be necessary.

3 The third decimal place in weight
Pupils should be familiar with the relationship

$$1000 \text{ g} = 1 \text{ kg}$$
Discuss: 1 g = 1 thousandth of a kilogram
$$= 0.001 \text{ kg}$$

Introductory activities 1 and 2 above could be repeated for weight to demonstrate relative weights using different packages. For example, nails, crisps, butter, sugar and so on.

Equipment

Calculator.
For the Introductory activities: measuring instruments for weight and volume, a selection of packages and containers which display volumes or weights.

73
Decimals 3:
The third
decimal place,
l/ml; kg/g

SM4a/5

RTN/E3
AS/E3

Content

- Interpretation of tables
- Position fixing
- Interpretation and application of a code
- Place value to thousandths, ordering
- Continuation of a number pattern.

Introductory activities

A set of digit cards (see **Equipment** list) is required.
The digit cards can be laid out on a desk if working with a group or stuck on a wall with 'Blu-Tack', if working with the whole class.

1 Place value: decimals
Use the digit cards, along with one showing the decimal point, to consolidate the concept of place value with tenths, hundredths, and thousandths. Emphasise:

- The decimal point shows where the units place can be found.
- The composition of the number. For example:

is 2 units + 3 tenths + 7 hundredths + 8 thousandths or 2 + 0.3 + 0.07 + 0.008

- The value of a particular digit depends on its place in the number. For example:

6 units ——
4 tenths ——
9 thousandths ——
2 hundredths ——

Several examples should be given including those with a zero digit, for example:
0.213, 1.045, 0.109, 2.150 and so on.

2 Place value: comparing numbers
Use the digit cards to compare pairs of numbers to find which one is the greater. For example:
'Which is greater, 3.427 or 3.472 ?'
Arrange the cards to form the numbers one below the other and compare digits from *left* to *right*.

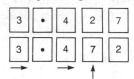

In this example the first difference is found in the hundredths:
7 is greater than 2, so 3.472 is greater than 3.427.
Several examples of this type should be considered.

Detailed notes

Table above Q1   Ensure pupils can interpret the table using the code.

Q4   See Introductory activity 2 above for layout and method.

Equipment

For the Introductory activities: two sets of digit cards (0 to 9) and two cards with a decimal point.

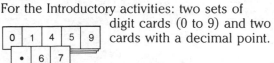

75

Decimals 3:
Place value
using a
calculator

N2a/5

PSE
RTN/E3
AS/E3

Content

- Interpretation of written information
- Place value to thousandths
- Addition and subtraction
- Problem solving: methodical working, trial and improvement.

Introductory activity

Adding and subtracting
Use the cards to display 2·352.
Discuss which number should be added to make, for example, 2·652. Talk in terms of 'add 3 in the tenths column. The number is 0·3.'

2	•	3	5	2
0	•	3		
2	•	6	5	2

Repeat to change 2·352 to 2·372 and 2·352 to 2·358.

Repeat this activity several times to demonstrate both addition and subtraction.

Detailed notes

Q1 'number' refers to tenths, hundredths or thousandths.

Q3 The numbered cards may be used to explain the stages. Some pupils may use a different order.

Equipment

Calculator.
For the Introductory activity: the digit cards used for the Introductory activities on Core Textbook page 74.

Calculator Game 1: Decimal checkout

Number of players Two.

Description
This game is for the input of units, tenths, hundredths and thousandths.

Player 1: Selects a starting number.
Player 2: Enters the starting number into the calculator and by a series of subtractions of units, tenths, hundredths or thousandths, reduces the starting number to zero.

The process is repeated with the second player providing a different starting number for the first player. A typical game is shown below.

The order of subtraction could be changed. The players will quickly realise that starting numbers which contain the digit zero require fewer subtractions, for example, 4·009 only requires two subtractions.
One point is given for each 'Checkout' completed without error.
The game could continue until one player has a score of, for example, 10.

Equipment for game

A calculator for each player.

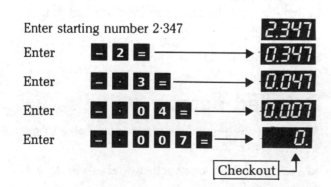

Enter starting number 2·347   2.347
Enter   − 2 = ⟶ 0.347
Enter   − · 3 = ⟶ 0.047
Enter   − · 0 4 = ⟶ 0.007
Enter   − · 0 0 7 = ⟶ 0.
Checkout

Calculator Game 2: Decimal place value

Number of players Two or more.

Description
Each player shuffles a set of digit cards and places them face down in a pile on the desk. In turn, each player takes the top card from his/her pile, declares whether it is to be units, tenths, hundredths or thousandths. He/she positions the digit card on the appropriate place on the notation card and enters the appropriate number on the calculator. For example:

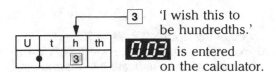

'I wish this to be hundredths.'

0.03 is entered on the calculator.

Each player in turn takes another digit card from his/her pile, positions it on the notation card and *adds* the value of that number to that already displayed on the calculator. The game continues until they each have a four-digit number. The winner is the player with the larger number. One point is given for a win. (The game could also be played where the smaller number wins.) A typical game is shown below.
The game could continue until one player has a score of, for example, 10.

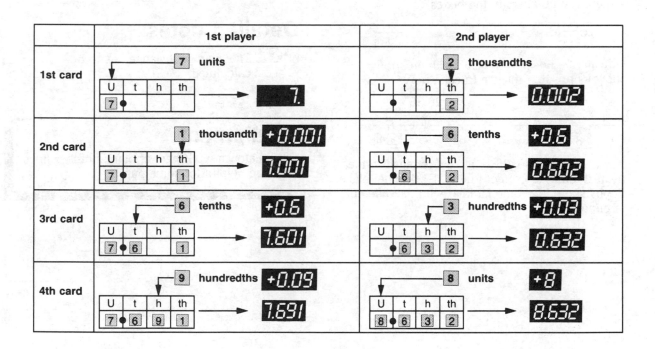

Equipment for game

For each player: a calculator, a set of digit cards numbered from 0 to 9, a notation card marked as shown.

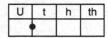

76
W30
Decimals 3:
Approximation
to first
decimal place

N4d/5 → 6

RTN/E3
AS/D3
MD/E4
RN/E1

Content

- Interpretation of tables
- Interpretation and completion of scales marked in hundredths
- Approximation to the first decimal place
- Calculation of an average.

Organisation

Pupils should attempt Q1 to Q5 after Introductory activity 1. Introductory activity 2 should then take place before the pupils complete Q6.

Introductory activities

1 Approximation to the first decimal place from two decimal places
Demonstrate how to round a number correct to the first decimal place, for example:
Round 26·38 to one decimal place.
A possible approach might be:
Draw a blank number line.
26·38 lies between 26·3 and 26·4.
Write these numbers in the boxes.

Indicate the position of 26·38 with an arrow.
Show its position relative to each box.

26·38

It is nearer 26·4 so, 26·38 is 26·4 rounded to the nearest tenth, or correct to the first decimal place. Pupils should become familiar with the different terminology.

This activity should be repeated for several examples. Some possible examples are:
2·76, 14·42, 25·06, 55·51, 16·98.

2 Approximation to the first decimal place from several decimal places
Draw a blank number line.
Ask pupils to divide 149 by 7 using a calculator.
149 ÷ 7 = 8·7647058
By discussion establish that the answer lies between 8·7 and 8·8.

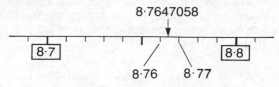

By counting from 8·7, 8·71, 8·72 and so on until 8·76, establish that the answer 8·7647058 is '8·76 and a bit', and so indicate the approximate position on the number line.

Continue as for Introductory activity 1 above.
Possible further examples are:
213 ÷ 14, 336 ÷ 13, 478 ÷ 65, 460 ÷ 18.

Detailed notes

Q4b The average distance has to be calculated.

Equipment

Calculator, a worksheet of blank number lines may be helpful for some pupils.

77	78, 79	W31, W32	80
Calculations	Bearings	Using a 360° protractor	Estimating and measuring

E24	E25
Bearings	Bearings

CONTENT AND DEVELOPMENT

Core

Pupils should have met angles and bearings and measured and constructed angles to the nearest 10°.

Angles 1 (on pages 60–62 of these notes) covered right, acute, obtuse, straight and reflex angles, sum of the angles of a triangle, horizontal, vertical, parallel and perpendicular lines.

Angles 2 consolidates and extends the work on angles and bearings, and covers:

- compass directions and three-figure bearings
- calculation of angles round a point
- measurement and drawing of angles to the nearest 5°.

Extension

E24 and E25 can be attempted on completion of Core Textbook page 80. They contain additional work on the use of bearings in navigation.

National Curriculum (England and Wales)

SM2d, 3a

Mathematics 5–14 (Scotland)

PFS/E3
A/C1, D1, D2

RELATED ACTIVITIES

1 Map work
Activities using an Ordnance Survey map and a compass or an Admiralty Chart and a compass, particularly if these show local areas, should be of interest to many pupils.

2 Orienteering
There may be opportunities for pupils to try orienteering as a sport. This is something they could be asked to investigate for themselves.

EQUIPMENT

Card, glue, scissors, ruler, cardboard, commercial 360° protractor, 'compass' protractor from W22.
For Introductory activities: magnetic compass, large cardboard demonstration 360° protractor.

Content

- Interpretation of the 8-point mariner's compass directions
- Calculation of angles involving right angles and angles round a point.

Introductory activity

Compass angles
Remind pupils of the right angles and half right angles between directions on an 8-point compass.

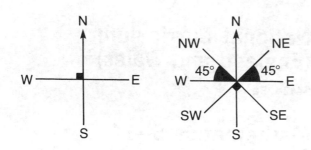

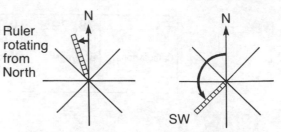

Ruler now pointing South West

Rotations could be shown by turning a ruler or pencil on top of a large drawing of a compass on a card or on the blackboard or on an OHP transparency. The diagrams above show an anti-clockwise rotation from North of $1\frac{1}{2}$ right angles, $(90° + 45° = 135°)$.

Demonstrate that this is the same direction as a clockwise turn of $2\frac{1}{2}$ right angles, $(90° + 90° + 45° = 225°)$.

Equipment
None.

Content

- Measurement of three-figure bearings to the nearest 5°.

Introductory activity

Introduction of three-figure bearings
Make a large cardboard protractor with 5° markings on the scale. Ask a pupil to use a magnetic compass to find the direction of North. Place the cardboard protractor on a table and position it with 000° pointing North. A ruler can be placed on top to point to North and can then be turned clockwise to point in the direction of a distant object. The direction or *bearing* of the object can be introduced as an *angle turned clockwise from North*.

The bearing should be found by counting on in 10° steps from 000°, 090°, 180°, or 270°. Emphasise that three figures are always used, for example, 080°, read as 'zero eight zero' or 'oh eight oh' degrees.

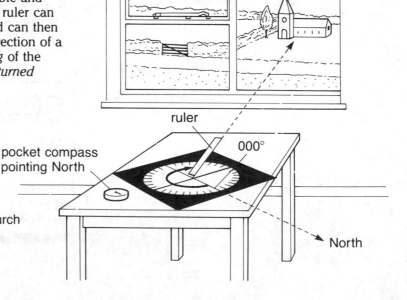

ruler

pocket compass pointing North

000°

North

Bearing of church is about 230°.

Detailed notes

Top of page 78 | Ensure pupils understand the information in each diagram above Q1.

Q3 | The normal convention is to put North at the top of a page. Pupils should be aware that this does not always happen in practice when working with maps and charts. Emphasise that they should check the position of North and not assume it is pointing to the top of the map.

Equipment
Card, glue, scissors, cardboard protractor from W22.
For the Introductory activity: magnetic compass, large cardboard demonstration 360° protractor.

Content

- Estimation of angle size
- Measurement and construction of angles to the nearest 5°.

Organisation

Introductory activities 1 and 2 should be done before W31. Introductory activity 3 is associated with W32.

Introductory activities

1 Estimation of angle size
Encourage pupils to estimate the size of an angle before they use a protractor to measure it. They should estimate the angle below as being more than 1 right angle but less than 2 right angles.

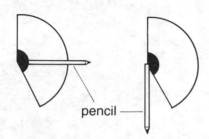
pencil

This should help them to read from the correct protractor scale.

2 Measuring angles
The circular protractor on W31 has been simplified so that only one scale is shown. The type of protractor which should be demonstrated is the one which is available to pupils. Many protractors are suitable for demonstration with an OHP.

Show pupils how to measure angles using the method recommended on W31. Several examples should be demonstrated before pupils start the work on the page.

3 Drawing angles
Show pupils how to draw angles using the method on W32. An initial line of about 6 cm is recommended. Encourage pupils to check their angle by estimating its size after its construction.

Equipment

Ruler, 360° protractor.

Content

- Estimation of angles
- Measurement and construction of angles to the nearest 5°.

Detailed notes

Q2e,f Check that pupils have drawn and marked the *reflex* angle.

Equipment

360° protractor.

Content

- Interpretation of a map
- Measurement of three-figure bearings to the nearest 5°.

Detailed notes

Q2 No marked lines are given. Pupils have to judge where the lines might be.

Q3 This is to stress the fact that North is 000°.

Q4a,b A range of answers is possible for both parts. Pupils are likely to work in 5° multiples but some may give more accurate bearings.

Equipment

Cardboard protractor from W22.

E25

Angles 2:
Bearings

SM2d/6;
3a/5 → 6

PFS/E3
A/D1, D2

Content

- Interpretation of a map
- Measurement of bearings to the nearest 5°
- Calculation of true distance from a map using a scale factor.

Additional activities

1 Local map
Pupils could make a similar map to the one on E24 for their local area. A compass may be needed for finding North.

2 Computer software
A wide range of commercial software is available for angle estimation and bearings.

Equipment

Cardboard protractor from W22, ruler.

Detailed notes

Q1 Pupils should work systematically by placing the protractor at A to find the bearing from A to B and then use a ruler to find the distance AB. The scale factor should then be used to find the true distance. The protractor should then be moved to B to take the next bearing, and so on.

Q2 Some pupils may see a relationship between the answers to Q1 and Q2, but it is not the intention to teach a rule for 'back bearings' at this stage.

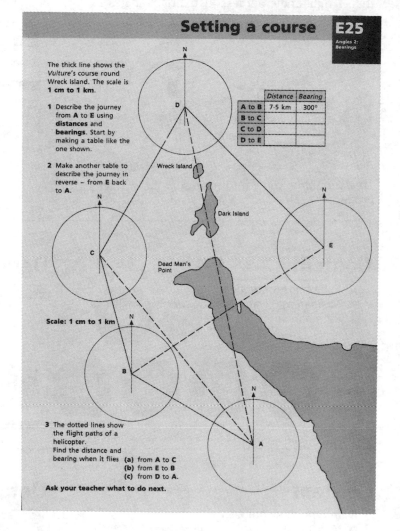

Setting a course — E25 Angles 2: Bearings

The thick line shows the *Vulture's* course round Wreck Island. The scale is **1 cm to 1 km**.

1 Describe the journey from **A** to **E** using **distances** and **bearings**. Start by making a table like the one shown.

	Distance	Bearing
A to B	7·5 km	300°
B to C		
C to D		
D to E		

2 Make another table to describe the journey in reverse – from **E** back to **A**.

Scale: 1 cm to 1 km

3 The dotted lines show the flight paths of a helicopter.
Find the distance and bearing when it flies (a) from **A** to **C**
(b) from **E** to **B**
(c) from **D** to **A**.

Ask your teacher what to do next.

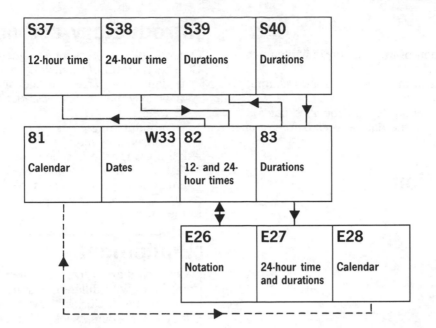

CONTENT AND DEVELOPMENT

Core

Previously pupils should have carried out work with am and pm times and have been introduced to 24-hour notation. It is assumed that they have calculated durations when these were mainly within the hour and that they have also written dates in a variety of formats.

In *Time*, this earlier work is consolidated and extended to cover:

- finding the date a week ahead or a week ago
- the use of a diary
- equating am and pm times to 24-hour notation and *vice versa*
- the use of transport timetables
- calculation of duration by 'counting on'.

Support

S37 and S38 provide a lead in to Core Textbook page 82. S39 and S40 provide a lead in to Core Textbook page 83.

S37 to S40 might also be used as a parallel unit on time instead of Core Textbook pages 82 and 83.

Extension

E28 extends the work of Core Textbook page 81. E26 provides extension for Core Textbook page 82. E27 extends the work on Core Textbook page 83 on durations.

Alternatively E27 and E28 may both be attempted after Core Textbook page 83.

National Curriculum (England and Wales)

UA4a
N4b
SM4a

Mathematics 5–14 (Scotland)

PSE
T/C1, C2, C4, D1, D2

RELATED ACTIVITIES

1 The time of our lives
Time in 24-hour notation, dates and durations are likely to occur in pupils' daily lives as they make journeys, borrow books from the library and look at TV guides, newspapers and magazines.

2 Where do the trains go?
Timetables can lead to interesting investigations about the distances and geographical positions of the places listed.

EQUIPMENT

Current diaries or calendars, envelopes with different postmarks, time lines with 12-hour and 24-hour notation (marked in 5 minute intervals), a time line or clock showing the 12/24 hour relationships, calculator.
For Introductory activities: sequences of daily newspapers, weekly and monthly magazines, card, felt pens, air, bus and train timetables, concert timetables.

Content

- Interpretation of information in written and visual form
- Knowledge of the order of months starting with any month
- Use of a calendar to find specified dates
- Calculation of the date a week before or after a given date.

Organisation

Pupils should work in groups.

Introductory activity

Ordering newspapers and magazines
Give each group of pupils one of these resources:
- daily newspapers for one week
- weekly magazines for about five consecutive weeks
- monthly magazines for about five consecutive months.

Ask the group to order the publications from the oldest to the most recent. Suggest each group retains one copy and passes the others to another group. The receiving group have to find the date of the missing copy.

Equipment

A current diary or calendar, a collection of envelopes with different postmarks.
For the Introductory activity: sequences of daily newspapers, weekly and monthly magazines.

Detailed notes

Q1 It is easier if pupils look at the dates of magazines at the bottom of the pile and work to the top.

Q2f A weekend is usually taken to mean Saturday and Sunday.

Q3 The required dates are best written in the same format as the one shown on the paper.

Q4 Pupils may be unsure what to call the number. 'Issue' or 'publication number' could be suggested.

Q6 Some pupils might need the help of a clue: 'Look at the issue or publication number.'

Q8 A current diary or calendar is required here.

Q10 The class collection could be sorted by year, month, geographical area, or the format in which the date is written.

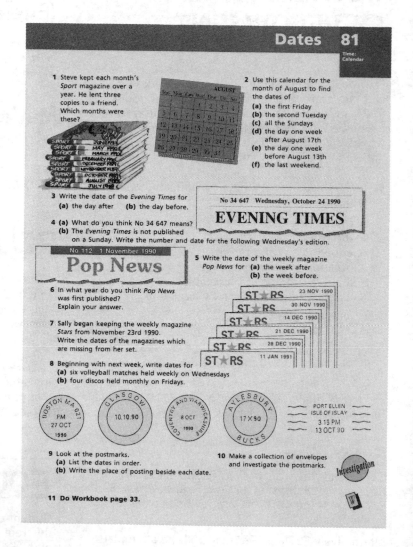

Content

- Making entries in a diary.

Introductory activity

Diaries
Ask a group to look at a few diaries where the layout is different and to report to others on the layouts used. Discuss with the pupils what type of entries can be made and how these might be written.

Detailed notes

Q2 Encourage the pupils to enter at least five events.

Additional activity

Famous diaries
Encourage pupils to find books in the library which are based on, or contain, reproductions of diary entries. They should note the method of recording the date and the layout used.

Equipment

For the Introductory activity: current diaries. These might be brought in by the pupils.

Content

- Relationship between am and pm times and 24-hour notation.

Organisation

Pupils should work in pairs.

Introductory activity

24-hour notation
Discuss the three different ways in which time is expressed:

1 as a display

2 speaking   'one forty-five' or 'quarter to two in the afternoon'

3 recording   1.45 pm or 13.45

The recording should lead to an investigation of 24-hour notation where midnight is considered as the start of the day, that is 0000 hours, and also as the finish of the day, that is 2400 hours. Ask the pupils how afternoon or pm times are expressed in this notation, for example, as 13.00, 14.00, 15.00 . . . . . 23.00 hours. The spoken expression 'thirteen hundred hours' can be misleading and requires a reminder that time is not based on a hundred minutes.

Detailed notes

Q1 Explain to pupils that the layout used for times and events in Q2 should be used as a model for the table in this question.

Q2 When pupils have completed Q1 they have, along with the table in Q2, the table for the whole day.

Equipment

None.

Content

■ Calculation of journey times by counting on from the starting time to the finishing time.

Introductory activity

A 24-hour time line

Ask pupils to make a time line which shows the hours and five minute interval marks for display on the classroom wall. If necessary, it may be restricted to show 0800 to 2200.

Use the time line to identify starting and finishing times. Discuss how the duration between two times might be found using the line. Contrast different ways, for example, of counting on by
- hours and then minutes
- minutes to the next hour, then hours and then minutes.

Ask pupils to illustrate the procedure to find answers for several examples using the technique they prefer.

Additional activity

Local timetables

Use train, bus or 'plane timetables to investigate real journey times. Air timetables are ideal for less-able pupils as the number of departure and arrival times is likely to be far fewer than for other modes of transport.

Equipment

For the Introductory activity: card and felt pens.
For the Additional activity: local train, bus and air timetables.

Detailed notes

Time line above Q1	Ask pupils what each mark between the hours represents.
Time-table beside Q1	Check that pupils understand why some place names appear twice.

Q6,7	These more demanding questions may be omitted by some pupils.

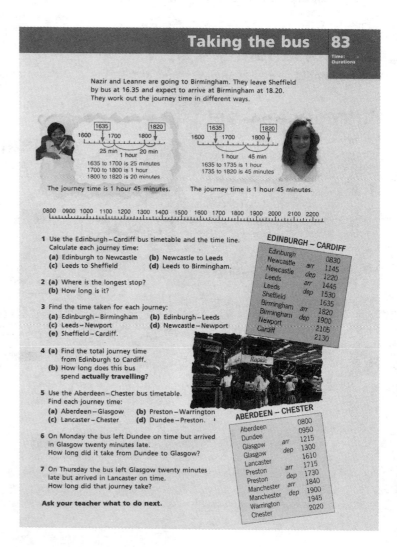

Content

- Interpretation of information presented in written form
- 12-hour times in words and notation.

Introductory activity

Concert timetables
Examples of concert timetables should be brought in by the pupils, for example, for school productions, local theatres or other venues. TV timetables could also be used. Some discussion of the timetables should take place, for example, how are morning and evening programmes distinguished? Examples from S37 given in 12-hour notation should be selected and written in both words and in 12-hour notation, for example:
Heatwave   1.55 pm   five minutes to two
                                    in the afternoon.

Detailed notes

Program-me beside Q1	Some help with interpretation may be required.
Q2	Ensure that there is at least some informal description of before or after noon, for example, 'in the morning'.

Equipment

For the Introductory activity: concert timetables (for example, school productions and local theatres).

S37
Time:
12-hour time

**SM4a/
3 → 4**

T/C1, C2

Content

- Reading digital times
- Conversion from 12-hour to 24-hour notation and *vice versa*.

Introductory activity

Relationship between 12-hour and 24-hour times
Some discussion of digital clocks should take place. Some pupils will have a digital watch, others an analogue watch. Examples of when each type of notation is used should be given, for example:

- 12-hour times – TV times, general use such as arranging to meet someone or booking a table in a restaurant
- 24-hour times – video recorders, timetables.

Pupils should be asked to write examples of times in their day in both 12-hour and 24-hour notation, for example, Breakfast   7.45 am and 0745. Examples from S37 should then be selected and written in both notations, for example:
Heatwave   1.55 pm and 1355.

Detailed notes

Q1	Pupils may need directing to the programme beside Q1 on S37.

Additional activity

Concert Programme - Saturday
Pupils adapt the programme beside Q1 on S37 to show the times in 24-hour notation.

Equipment

None.

S38
Time:
24-hour time

SM4a/4

T/D1

N4b/4
SM4a/
3 → 4

T/C1, C2,
D2

Content

- Methodical working, recording findings in written form
- 12-hour times and the relationships between hours and minutes
- Time calculations
  - given starting time and duration, find finishing time
  - given starting and finishing times, find durations.
  All durations are multiples of five minutes.

Introductory activity

'Counting on' or 'counting back'
Methods of 'counting on' or 'counting back' on a time line should be discussed with the pupils. For example, using the programme for the Saturday concert:
Geraldine falls 1 hour 40 minutes after her act started. When did she fall?

3.35 pm and 1 hour is 4.35 pm
4.35 pm and 40 min is 5.15 pm
She fell at 5.15 pm.
or
3.35 pm and 25 min is 4.00 pm
4.00 pm and 1 hour is 5.00 pm
5.00 pm and 15 min is 5.15 pm
She fell at 5.15 pm

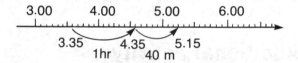

How long was Heatwave on stage?

1.55 pm to 2.00 pm is 5 min
2.00 pm to 2.40 pm is 40 min
That makes 45 minutes altogether.

Detailed notes

Time line above Q1 Explain that this is one time line with 3.00 repeated.

Q4 Less able pupils may need to work in pairs.

Equipment
None.

N4b/4
SM4a/4

T/D1, D2

Content

- 24-hour notation and the relationship between hours and minutes
- Time calculations
  - given starting time and duration, find finishing time
  - given starting and finishing times, find durations
  All durations are multiples of five minutes.

Introductory activity

'Counting on' or 'counting back'
Questions similar to those for S39 should be discussed using 24-hour notation.

Detailed notes

Time line above Q1 Explain that this is one time line with 1400 repeated.

Q3,4 Emphasise that answers should be in 24-hour notation.

Equipment
None.

Content

■ Interpretation of information presented in written form
■ Relationship between am and pm times and 24-hour notation.

Detailed notes

Q1 The notice board and diary entries have to be studied before the question can be answered.

Q2 The watch displays illustrated show the month before the day. Discuss the various displays on different watches.

Q4 Pupils may find it helpful to consider their answer to Q1. Possible explanations are, for example, the dental appointment may take longer than expected, if he goes to the football he won't get home in time.

Equipment

None.

E26
Time:
Notation

SM4a/4

T/D1

Content

■ Relationship between am and pm times and 24-hour notation
■ Rounding times to the nearest quarter hour
■ Use of rounded times to calculate durations.

Detailed notes

Table above Q1 A discussion could include
■ reasons for such a table, for example, for motorists to know times to put their car lights on, for cyclists without lights to know when to be off the streets
■ reasons for the time differences, for example, the further East a location, the earlier the sunrise.

Q8 The times should be rounded to the nearest quarter hour and written in words.

Q10 Pupils should notice 1823 and 0926 (show nearly the same number of minutes) and need only consider the hours in their calculation.

Q11 Pupils should be asked to explain their answers.

Equipment

None.

E27
Time:
24-hour time and durations

N4b/4
SM4a/4

T/D1, D2

Content

■ Interpretation of information presented in written and visual form
■ The use of a calendar.
The work is set in three different contexts, the most difficult being Timeshare.

Detailed notes

Q5 The year prior to the current year may be involved.

Q6 to Q11 The idea of Timeshare should be discussed before pupils attempt these questions.
■ A Timeshare week runs from Saturday to Saturday.
■ Week 1 in the Timeshare year does not always begin on January 1st.

Equipment

A current diary or calendar, calculator.

E28
Time:
Calendar

N4b/5
SM4a/4

PSE
T/C4

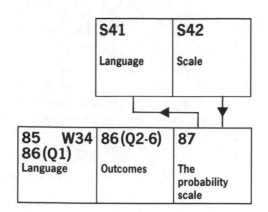

S41 Language	S42 Scale

85 W34 86 (Q1) Language	86 (Q2-6) Outcomes	87 The probability scale

CONTENT AND DEVELOPMENT

Core

As many pupils experience difficulty with the concepts in this area of mathematics, the development of Probability in Heinemann Mathematics 7 is gradual and, in the main, provides consolidation of ideas likely to have been met previously.

The section covers:

- placing events in order of likelihood using impossible, certain, less/more likely, least/most likely
- listing all the possible outcomes for an event
- using the probability scale – impossible (0), poor chance (less than $\frac{1}{2}$), even chance ($\frac{1}{2}$), good chance (greater than $\frac{1}{2}$), certain (1).

Throughout the section pupils carry out a number of practical experiments designed to enhance their understanding of these ideas.

Support

S41 and S42 provide lead-in activities for Core Textbook page 87. They may be considered appropriate for a wider range of pupils than is usual for support of this nature.

National Curriculum (England and Wales)

HD3abde

Mathematics 5–14 (Scotland)

E+

EQUIPMENT

Playing cards, 1p coins, dice, counters in two colours (red and green preferred), opaque polythene bags, coloured pencils, blank paper.
For Introductory activities: die, coin, ten prepared letter cards.

Content

- Placing events in order of likelihood using the terms impossible, certain, less/more likely (comparing two events), least/most likely (ordering three events)
- Use of the terms poor chance, even chance, good chance.

When placing events in order both general knowledge and the results of practical experiments are used.

Organisation

Pupils should carry out the practical experiments in pairs. Some clarification of procedure and methods of recording may be necessary.

Introductory activity

More/most/less/least likely
Discuss with the pupils events within their experience or knowledge and ask them to decide comparative likelihoods. For example:

- 'sunbathing in summer' is more likely than 'sunbathing in winter' and *vice versa*
- you are at home and the telephone rings. Which is least/most likely: it is for you, it is for someone else, it is a wrong number?

Detailed notes

Q4b 'Certain' is appropriate in Britain. Some pupils may wish to consider a different location such as 'near the North Pole'.

W34, last question Pupils may find it difficult to give a succinct explanation. An understanding of the idea of 'evens' is assumed. In the colour experiment $\frac{1}{2}$ the cards are of the chosen colour so there is an even chance of guessing correctly. In the suit experiment only $\frac{1}{4}$ of the cards are of the chosen suit so the chance of guessing correctly is described as less than even or poor, and so on.

Additional activity

Poor/even/good chance
Prepare ten letter cards as shown.

Display in a row the terms no chance/impossible, poor chance/less than even, even chance, good chance/greater than even, certain.
The pupils should choose from these terms in order to answer questions of the following type.
A blindfolded person picks a card at random, what is the chance of picking an A, an E, an I, a vowel, an F ?

Equipment

Playing cards, 1p coins.
For the Additional activity: ten prepared letter cards (5As, 3Es, 2Is).

Content

- Listing outcomes of an event found by experimentation
- Listing all the possible outcomes of an event.

Introductory activities

1 The terms 'event' and 'outcome'
Revise 'event' and 'outcome' by discussing a variety of examples such as:

Event	Outcome
Tossing a coin	head, tail
Arriving at school	early, on time, late
Rolling a die	1,2,3,4,5,6

2 Listing outcomes
One pupil should be given a die numbered 1 to 6 and another pupil a coin. Ask one pupil to roll the die while the other tosses the coin. Record the outcome in a table. For example,

would be recorded as

Number on die	Coin
5	H

The experiment should be repeated, say six or seven times. Ask individual pupils to identify outcomes which are the same and to suggest possible outcomes which may not have occurred in the experiments.

Detailed notes

Q2c Encourage the pupils to make a systematic list.

Additional activity

Outcomes of tossing three coins
All the possible outcomes of tossing a 2p coin, a 5p coin and a 10p coin could be listed. Pupils may need help in devising a systematic form of recording as shown.

2p	5p	10p
H	H	H
H	H	T
H	T	H
		and so on.

Some may be able to use a more concise form such as (H,H,H).

Equipment

Dice, counters in two colours (red and green preferred), opaque polythene bags.
For Introductory activity 2: die, coin.

Content

- Language of probability for two equally likely outcomes – even chance, 1 in 2, or $\frac{1}{2}$
- Probability descriptions and their positions on the probability scale – impossible (0), poor chance (less than $\frac{1}{2}$), good chance (greater than $\frac{1}{2}$), certain (1).

Introductory activity

Linking chance and the probability scale
Repeat the Additional activity for Core Textbook page 85 using the ten letter cards. Each word answer should be located on a probability scale and expressed numerically using 0, less than $\frac{1}{2}$, $\frac{1}{2}$, greater than $\frac{1}{2}$, 1.

Chance ⟶	impossible	poor chance	evens	good chance	certain
Probability ⟶	0	less than $\frac{1}{2}$	$\frac{1}{2}$	greater than $\frac{1}{2}$	1

For example, the chance of picking an E is poor; the probability of picking an E is less than $\frac{1}{2}$. This activity could be repeated using twelve vehicle cards consisting of 3 red and 3 blue cars, 1 green and 3 red buses, 2 red vans.

Detailed notes

Panel above Q1	Most pupils should benefit from a discussion about coin tossing in which this language is used.

Additional activity

Different dice
Pupils could be challenged to make a cube, draw pictures of objects on its faces and use it as a die. The pictures should be chosen so that, for example, when the die is rolled one of the outcomes has a probability of $\frac{1}{2}$ (3 faces showing triangles) and another outcome has a probability of less than $\frac{1}{2}$/more than $\frac{1}{2}$ (2 faces showing green shapes/4 faces showing blue shapes).
The pupils might try to describe outcomes that would be impossible (for example, showing a sphere) or certain (for example, showing a shape).

Equipment

For the Introductory activity: ten prepared letter cards (5As, 3Es, 2Is) as used in the Additional activity on Core Textbook page 85.

Content

Language of probability:
- for two equally likely outcomes – even chance, probability of 1 in 2
- impossible, certain, at random.

Introductory activity

Identikit
Ask the pupils to draw a football player with either dark hair or fair hair, either blue eyes or brown eyes, either a red strip or a blue strip. Each pupil should guess what the player drawn by a neighbour will look like. They should realise, from the given instructions, that for each drawing
- 'showing a football player' is *certain*
- there is an *even chance* of 'the player having fair hair/blue eyes/red strip/etc.'
- 'a player having red hair/green eyes/white strip/etc.' is *impossible*.

Detailed notes

Q1	Following the instructions one pupil should draw the head and shoulders of a person in the rectangle and then cover the drawing with paper as the other partner answers part (b). The instructions must always be visible.
Q2a	Pupils could discuss this as a pair before completing the drawings. They need to realise that the expressions 'even chance' and 'a probability of 1 in 2' both imply that half of the drawings must show the named feature.
Q2b, second blob	Pupils should realise that many answers are possible here.

Equipment

Coloured pencils including blue, brown and red, blank paper.

Content

- Relationships between probabilities 0, $\frac{1}{2}$ and 1 and the descriptors impossible, even chance, certain.

Organisation

Pupils should work in pairs to discuss each question before completing their own drawings.

Equipment

None.

Detailed notes

Q1 It may be necessary to emphasise that in (a) pupils look at each pair of doors in turn while for (b) all six doors are to be considered.

Q2 Some pupils may need reminding that a probability of 1 means that all have the feature (certain), that 0 means none have it (impossible), and that $\frac{1}{2}$ means half have it (even chance).

Q3 Pupils should look at the completed houses of classmates and realise a wide range of combinations of features can meet the requirements.

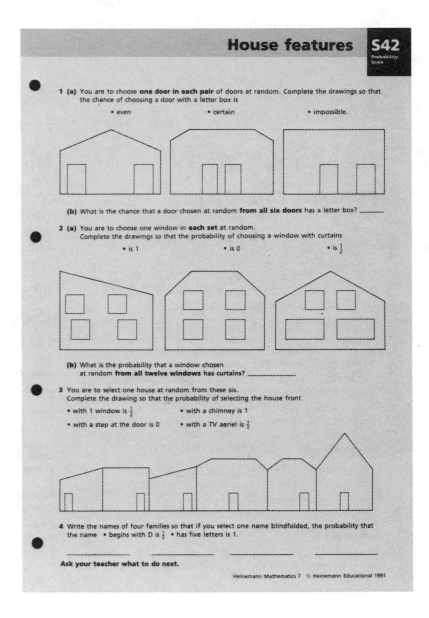

House features **S42**
Probability:
Scale

1 (a) You are to choose **one door in each pair** of doors at random. Complete the drawings so that the chance of choosing a door with a letter box is
- even
- certain
- impossible.

(b) What is the chance that a door chosen at random **from all six doors** has a letter box? _____

2 (a) You are to choose one window in **each set** at random.
Complete the drawings so that the probability of choosing a window with curtains
- is 1
- is 0
- is $\frac{1}{2}$

(b) What is the probability that a window chosen at random **from all twelve windows** has curtains? _____

3 You are to select one house at random from these six.
Complete the drawing so that the probability of selecting the house front
- with 1 window is $\frac{1}{2}$
- with a chimney is 1
- with a step at the door is 0
- with a TV aerial is $\frac{1}{2}$

4 Write the names of four families so that if you select one name blindfolded, the probability that the name
- begins with D is $\frac{1}{2}$
- has five letters is 1.

_____ _____ _____ _____

Ask your teacher what to do next.

Heinemann Mathematics 7 © Heinemann Educational 1991

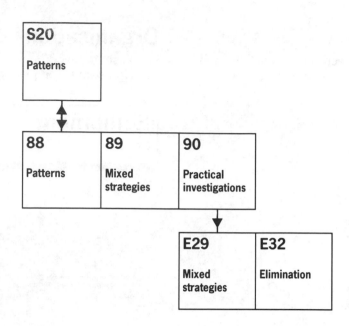

CONTENT AND DEVELOPMENT

Core

Although individual questions on pages throughout Heinemann Mathematics involve problem solving, there are two specific sections of work labelled 'problem solving' in Heinemann Mathematics 7.

Problem solving 1 (on pages 32–35 of these notes) gave pupils the opportunity to use 'guess, check and improve' (trial and improvement) and 'listing' strategies. In this section the strategy of 'looking for a pattern' is met as well as consolidating the strategies already being used.

Support

S20 may be used to introduce pupils to the strategy of 'search for a pattern' as a lead-in to Core Textbook page 88.

Extension

The strategy of 'elimination' is focussed on as well as consolidation of other strategies, particularly 'listing'.

National Curriculum (England and Wales)

UA2abc, 4d
A2b
SM3d

Mathematics 5–14 (Scotland)

PSE
PD/D1, E2
PFS/E3

EQUIPMENT

Range of newspapers with double-page sheets only, sticks or straws of equal length, other materials such as squares, cubes, pegs and pegboard, squared paper, coloured pencils, marbles, six 36 cm strips of card, sticky tape, notepaper, envelopes, card (A4), scissors, glue, ball, about 500 cm³ of sand (or salt/sugar), ruler, pipe-cleaner or string to measure a curved length.

88
Problem
solving 2:
Patterns

A2b/4

PSE
PS/D1, E2

Content

- Recognition of number patterns including those developed from spatial arrangements
- Prediction of subsequent numbers in a pattern
- Construction of a number pattern and describing it in words.

Organisation

Pupils should work in pairs.

Introductory activity

Patterns in numbers
Discuss with pupils number patterns which occur in various situations, for example:

- right-hand pages in books are often odd numbered
- every fourth year is a leap year and is divisible by 4
- dates of a specific day in a calendar month 'jump' by 7 – 3, 10, 17, 24, 31.

Detailed notes

Q1 Pupils may predict the answer either by noticing:
- the pattern of increase in the row totals

$$\underbrace{1 \quad \underbrace{\quad}_{+3} \quad 4 \quad \underbrace{\quad}_{+5} \quad 9 \quad \underbrace{\quad}_{+7} \quad 16}$$

- or that the row total is the square of the row number
  row 4 → total 4× 4 or 16

Q2c Pupils should find that the sum of the two page numbers on the same side of every double-page sheet is always one more than the total number of pages.

Q4 Squares, cubes, counters, pegs on pegboards, coloured squares on squared paper are a few of the materials which pupils could use.

Equipment

Range of newspapers with double-page sheets only, sticks or straws of equal length, other materials such as squares, cubes, pegs and pegboard, squared paper, coloured pencils.

89
Problem
solving 2:
Mixed
strategies

UA2ac/5

PSE

Content

- Interpretation of information in written and tabular form
- Use of problem solving strategies including listing systematically and trial and improvement.

Organisation

Pupils should work in pairs.

Detailed notes

Q2b Pupils must identify the two teams whose 'matches played' increased between 7th and 14th March and realise that they played each other.

Q5 Pupils could be asked to explain to others, or write about, how they found their answers. For example: 'We knew the points gained for third place was 3. We subtracted this from 20, giving 17. Three first places and one second place give 17.'

Q6 'The total number of points available is $(6 \times 5) + (6 \times 2) + (6 \times 1)$, that is 48. If Gladeside scored 20, then Hillgrange scored 28.' Other methods of solution are, of course, possible and should also be discussed.

Equipment

None.

90
Problem
solving 2:
Practical
investigations

UA2b/5

PSE

Content

■ Construction of containers to meet specific requirements.

Organistion

Form eight groups and give each group one of the activities. This should provide comparisons between two groups for each activity.

Equipment

Marbles, six 36 cm strips of card, sticky tape, notepaper, envelopes, card (A4), scissors, glue, ball, about 500 cm³ of sand (or salt/sugar).

Detailed notes

Q1c Other shapes which could be made from the strips are square, rectangle, rhombus, trapezium/kite and circle. Underlying this investigation is the idea of maximum area enclosed by a fixed perimeter.

Q2 Gift wrapping paper could be provided as an alternative to card to make the folder. Some pupils may use the design of the envelope and enlarge it to make their folder.

Q3 Measuring the diameter of the ball is usually the main challenge here.

Q4 Restricting the card to an A4 sheet places the emphasis on planning the dimensions of the container so that it can be made from the available card and still have the specified volume.

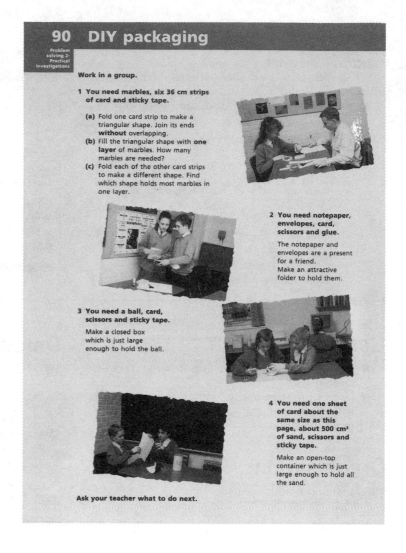

90 DIY packaging

Problem
solving 2:
Practical
investigations

Work in a group.

1 You need marbles, six 36 cm strips of card and sticky tape.

(a) Fold one card strip to make a triangular shape. Join its ends **without** overlapping.
(b) Fill the triangular shape with **one layer** of marbles. How many marbles are needed?
(c) Fold each of the other card strips to make a different shape. Find which shape holds most marbles in one layer.

2 You need notepaper, envelopes, card, scissors and glue.

The notepaper and envelopes are a present for a friend.
Make an attractive folder to hold them.

3 You need a ball, card, scissors and sticky tape.

Make a closed box which is just large enough to hold the ball.

4 You need one sheet of card about the same size as this page, about 500 cm³ of sand, scissors and sticky tape.

Make an open-top container which is just large enough to hold all the sand.

Ask your teacher what to do next.

Content

- Recognition of number patterns through spatial arrangements
- Prediction of subsequent numbers in a pattern.

Organisation

Pupils should work in pairs to discuss questions, making recordings on one sheet only.

Detailed notes

Q1 Pupils should be asked to try to complete the table for letters 1 to 5 after finishing the drawings. Thereafter a discussion about the sequence of number dots 3, 5, 7, 9, 11 should conclude that the number of dots increases by two each time. Hence the number of dots on each of the other letters can be found by *extending this sequence*.

The missing numbers could also be found by discovering the relationship between the 'number of the letter' and the 'number of dots on a letter', that is:

$$\text{number of dots on letter} = 2 \times \text{number of letter} + 1$$

This may be rather sophisticated for pupils at this level although some may recognise the spatial arrangement of the dots as 'n pairs plus 1' (for the nth letter).

Equipment

None.

Content

- Recognition of number patterns and prediction of subsequent numbers
- Describing number patterns in words
- Interpretation of information presented in written and visual form
- Use of problem solving strategies including systematic listing.

Detailed notes

Q4a The answers to Q2 and Q3 are used to complete the table.

Q4b Only a simple description is expected, for example, 'add on 2, then 3' and so on.

Q5 It may be necessary to emphasise that two copies of the same book can be chosen.

Q5c Pupils may give the answer 'you add on the number of books'. While this is correct, they should also realise that it is the same pattern starting at 3 rather than 1.

Equipment

None.

E29
Problem solving 2: Mixed strategies

UA2abc/5
A2b/4

PSE
PS/D1, E2

Content

- Calculation of true distances using scale
- Use of the problem solving strategy of elimination
- Interpretation of information in written and visual form.

Detailed notes

Q1 Pupils must realise that both distance and direction need to be checked.

Q2c As the road from TILT to CROY cannot be measured directly with a ruler, pupils should select a flexible material like a pipe-cleaner or string.

Equipment

Ruler, pipe-cleaner or string to measure a curved length.

E32
Problem solving 2: Elimination

UA2bc, 4d/5
SM3d/ 5 → 6

PSE
PFS/E3

DETOURS IN PART 3

General advice about using the Detours can be found on page T6 of these notes.

84
Detour:
Pounds/
kilograms,
miles/
kilometres

SM4a/5

D/E1
I/D1
ME/D9

Content

■ Approximate relationships between metric and imperial units of weight and length
■ Construction and interpretation of straight-line conversion graphs.

Introductory activity

Metric/imperial units
There should be a brief discussion about 'old' or imperial units still in everyday use especially pounds and miles. Pupils could be asked to collect examples of dual labelling in weight (food packaging) and length (maps and plans, sizes on clothes) and use these for a wall display. The approximate relationships – 1 lb is about $\frac{1}{2}$ kg, 5 miles is about 8 km, 1 mile is about 1·6 km – should be established and the use of the abbreviation lb highlighted.

Detailed notes

Panels above Q1 and Q4 — Pupils should record the relationship panels for future reference.

Q1b — Pupils should use the graph scales shown in the illustration beside the question. Some assistance may be required to interpret the Weight axis in particular.

Q4b — Pupils should use the graph scales shown in the illustration.

Equipment

2 mm squared paper, ruler.
For the Introductory activity: labels showing weight in kg and lb, maps with miles/km conversion information.

S35
Detour:
Shapes within
shapes

SM2ab/4

RS/D2, D3

Content

■ Construction and identification of triangles, quadrilaterals, pentagons, hexagons.
In this investigation pupils identify named shapes which have been constructed by drawing all the diagonals of a pentagon or hexagon.

Introductory activity

Naming shapes
Display a set of large paper or card shapes and discuss them with the pupils to remind them of the shape names and their side, angle and symmetry properties.
The shapes required are: isosceles and equilateral triangles, square, rectangle, rhombus, kite, trapezium, pentagon and hexagon.
Explain that the pentagons and hexagons on S35 are special as they are regular, that is, all their sides and angles are equal. Each named shape should be treated as distinct – it is not intended that there should be any explanation that, for example, a square is also a rectangle, rhombus, and so on.

Detailed notes

Q1 — Although the pupils should be able to identify the shapes perceptually, some may wish to confirm equality of sides by measurement.

Q3 — Pupils should check that they have drawn all the diagonals by referring to the shapes in Q1 and Q2.

Additional activity

More shapes within shapes
Prepared sheets of regular pentagons and hexagons, some with diagonals drawn, can be used for recording purposes for a variety of activities. For example:

■ Draw this coloured pattern. Name the shapes which are coloured

■ One isosceles triangle has been coloured. Colour two other *different* isosceles triangles.

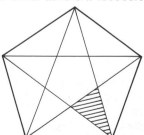

Equipment

Coloured pencils.
For the Introductory activity: prepared card shapes.
For the Additional activity: prepared duplicated sheets of regular pentagons and hexagons.

116

S36
Detour:
Overlap
shapes

SM2ab/4

PSE
RS/D2

Content

- Construction and identification of triangles, quadrilaterals, pentagons, hexagons.

In this investigation pupils identify named shapes which have been constructed by overlapping two congruent equilateral triangles.

Detailed notes

Q2 Some pupils may find it easier to cut out the traced triangle and work with this. They should then have little difficulty in marking the positions of the corners.

Q3 The pupils overlap shapes should also be based upon the two triangles. They could include a smaller equilateral triangle, a right-angled triangle, a quadrilateral and so on.

Additional activity

Overlap squares

A similar investigation could be carried out using a square as the starting shape. Pupils should be able to find shapes with from three to eight sides. A regular octagon is possible.

Equipment

Tracing paper, coloured pencils, scissors.

E33
Detour:
Distance
tables

UA3bd/5

ME/D9
PFS/E3

Content

- Interpretation and construction of distance tables using miles and kilometres
- Interpretation of information from a map
- Calculation of true distances from a map.

Detailed notes

Q3 The routes on the map should be matched with string (or other flexible material) which can then be straightened and measured *to the nearest centimetre*. Thereafter the true distances can be calculated using the scale.

Q4 The distances in the table can be either in miles or kilometres.

Equipment

Ruler, string or thread or pipe-cleaner.

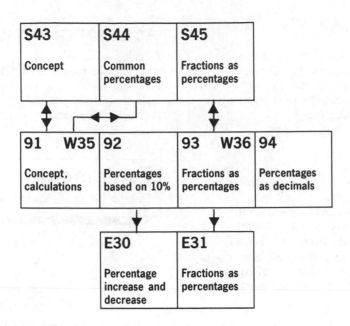

CONTENT AND DEVELOPMENT

Core

Previous work on percentages included the meaning of a percentage, expressing percentages as vulgar fractions (for example, $25\% = \frac{1}{4}$), realising that 100% of something means the whole of it, and simple calculations involving percentages (for example, 20% of 50).

In *Percentages*, this work is revised and then extended to cover:

- calculations involving percentages based on 10%
- expression of vulgar fractions as percentages
- expression of one quantity as a percentage of another
- expression of percentages in decimal form
- calculations involving percentages using a calculator.

Support

S43 and S44 can be used as a lead-in or parallel work for Core Textbook page 91. S45 relates to Core Textbook page 93 and can be used as either lead-in or parallel work.

Extension

E30 extends the work of Core Textbook page 92 to include percentage increase and decrease. E31 extends the work of Core Textbook page 93.

National Curriculum (England and Wales)

N2b, 3cd
HD2c

Mathematics 5–14 (Scotland)

PSE	**RTN/D4, E**	**D/E2**
I/D1, E1	**FPR/E1, E2, E3**	**E+**

RELATED ACTIVITIES

Work involving percentages is to be found in other sections, for example, *Handling Data*, *Extended Contexts* and so on. Percentages often occur in work in other subject areas, for example, Geography and Science.

Opportunity should be taken to discuss any percentage work relating to articles found in newspapers or magazines, for example 'New car sales fall by 10%'.

EQUIPMENT

Coloured pencils, scissors.
For an Introductory activity: 1 cm squared paper, coloured pencils, scissors.
For an Additional activity: $\frac{1}{2}$ cm and 1 cm squared paper.

91
W35
Percentages:
Concept,
calculations

N2b/4;
3c/4 → 5

RTN/D4
FPR/E1, E3

Content

- Expressing n parts in 100 as $n\%$
- Representation of a given percentage by colouring diagrams
- Meaning of 100% of something as the whole of it
- Simple vulgar fractional equivalents of percentages
- Calculation of simple percentages of quantities.

Organisation

Q1 to Q4 should be attempted after Introductory activity 1 and Q5 to Q8 after Introductory activities 2 and 3.

Introductory activities

1 (a) Meaning of a percentage
Use a prepared blackboard, wallchart or OHP diagram, as shown below, for discussion.

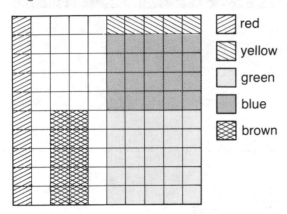

◨ red

◨ yellow

☐ green

■ blue

▨ brown

Establish that 'per cent' means per hundred and that the short-hand way of writing 'per cent' is %.

Since 10 small squares out of the hundred ($\frac{10}{100}$) are coloured red, then 10% are red.

Pupils could be asked to say what percentage of the large square is green, yellow and so on.

(b) 100% as the whole of something
Establish that if the whole square was coloured then 100 small squares out of 100 would be coloured or 100% would be coloured.
100% of something is the whole of it. Therefore, if 60% of the square is coloured than $(100 - 60)\%$ or 40% is not coloured.

2 Fractional equivalents for 10%, 20%, 25%, 50%, 75%
The vulgar fraction equivalents of the percentages in the REMEMBER panel should be committed to memory. Pupils should be reminded, by simplification of fractions, how these equivalences are established. For example:

$$20\% = \overset{\div 5}{\overbrace{\frac{20}{100}}_{\div 5}} = \overset{\div 4}{\overbrace{\frac{4}{20}}_{\div 4}} = \frac{1}{5}$$

3 10%, 20%, 25% and 50% of a quantity
There should be some discussion as to how to attempt this type of question. For example:
There are 200 pupils in Year 1 and 25% go home for lunch. How many go home for lunch?

$$25\% = \tfrac{1}{4} \quad \begin{aligned} &25\% \text{ of } 200 \\ &= \tfrac{1}{4} \text{ of } 200 \\ &= 50 \end{aligned} \qquad \dfrac{50}{4\overline{)200}}$$

50 pupils go home for lunch.

Detailed notes

Q6,7   Pupils who do not remember the fractional equivalent of the percentage could refer to the panel above Q6 before recording as in the worked example.

Equipment

Coloured pencils.

92
Percentages:
Percentages
based on 10%

N2b/4;
3c/4 → 5

RTN/D4
FPR/E3

Content

- Calculation of percentages of quantities.

Introductory activity

Using 10% as a basis for calculating certain percentages
The following examples could be used to establish the method used in Q3 to Q6.

(a) Find 70% of 320
    10% of 320 = 32
$7 \times 10\%$ → 70% of 320 = 7×32 = 224

(b) Find 5% of 800
    10% of 800 = 80
$\tfrac{1}{2}$ of 10% → 5% of 800 = $\tfrac{1}{2}$ of 80 = 40

(c) Find 15% of 140
    10% of 140 = 14
     5% of 140 = 7
$10\% + 5\%$ → 15% of 140 = 21

Detailed notes

Q1,2   These are revision questions based on known fractional equivalents of 10%, 20%, 25% and 50%.

Equipment

None.

93
W36
Percentages:
Fractions as
percentages

N3d/6
HD2c/
5 → 6

D/E2
I/D1
RTN/E
E+

Content

- Interpretation of bar graphs
- Expression of fractions with denominators 20, 25 or 50 as percentages
- Expression of one number as a percentage of another using equivalent fractions
- Construction of pie charts.

Introductory activity

TV facts
Pupils may need some revision work before they attempt this page. The following examples could be used to show how fractions with denominators 20, 25 or 50 can be expressed as percentages using equivalent fractions.

$\frac{8}{25}$ watched snooker

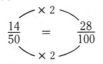

$$\frac{8}{25} = \frac{32}{100} \qquad 32\% \text{ watched snooker}$$

(b) A survey showed that 14 out of 50 people had more than one TV.

$\frac{14}{50}$ had more than one TV

$$\frac{14}{50} = \frac{28}{100} \qquad 28\% \text{ had more than one TV}$$

Detailed notes

Q7 Pupils have to find the total number of fish first.

W36, pie charts Pupils should colour the completed pie charts using different colours for each sector.

Additional activity

Surveys
Pupils could carry out surveys of their own and express the results as percentages. For example, on how they travel to school – walk, bus, car, cycle. The number of pupils surveyed should be 20, 25 or 50.

Equipment

Coloured pencils.

94
Percentages:
Percentages
as decimals

N3c/5;
2b/5 → 6

RTN/D4, E
FPR/E2

Content

- Percentages in decimal form
- Calculation of percentages of quantities.
Calculations are carried out using a calculator by entering the percentage in decimal form.

Introductory activities

1 Converting a percentage to a decimal fraction
A class or group discussion could focus on examples like these:
(a) 32% means 32 hundredths, so 32% = 0·32
(b) 6% means 6 hundredths, so 6% = 0·06
(c) 60% means 60 hundredths, so 60% = 0·60
The pupils should then be given oral practice in giving the decimal fraction equivalents of given percentages.

2 Finding percentages of quantities
The following two examples should be used to demonstrate the suggested method for using a calculator to find a percentage of a quantity.

(a) A school has 800 pupils. 49% of the pupils are girls.
How many girls are there?
To find 49% of 800,
Enter `0.49`   Press `× 8 0 0 =`
to give `392`

There are 392 girls.
(b) Find 7% of £480.
Enter `0.07`   Press `× 4 8 0 =`
to give `33.6`

So 7% of £480 = £33·60

Pupils may need reminding that 33·6 = 33·60 which gives £33.60

Detailed notes

Q4 Check that the correct answer for the area of lawns (2700 m²) has been given since Q5 depends on this.

Q5 Check that the correct answer for the weight of sand (270 kg or 270 000 g) has been given since Q6 depends on this.

Equipment

Coloured pencils.

Content

- Expressing *n* parts in 100 as *n*%
- Representation of a given percentage by colouring diagrams
- Meaning of 100% of something as the whole of it.

Introductory activities

1 Meaning of percentage
Work described in Introductory activity 1a for Core Textbook page 91 may be carried out.

2 Game shows
Many pupils will be familiar with the television 'game shows' which provide the context for the work on this page. These could be discussed briefly to set the scene. It may be easier to identify the titles of the game shows in Q1 if the workbook is held at a distance.
Pupils may be able to identify the game show Family Fortunes which provides the basis for Q2.

Detailed notes

Q2, line 2 The boundaries for the coloured parts should be determined perceptually. Pupils must know that '100% of something is the whole of it'.

Additional activity

More game shows
The pupils can draw 5 by 20 rectangles on $\frac{1}{2}$ cm or 1 cm squared paper and sketch display panels for game shows of their choosing. They should record the percentage of lights on etc. as in Q1.

Equipment

Coloured pencils.
For the Additional activity: $\frac{1}{2}$ cm or 1cm squared paper.

Content

- 50%, 25%, 10% in common fraction form
- 50%, 25%, 10% of a quantity by mental division.

Introductory activities

1 Equivalence of 50% and $\frac{1}{2}$, 25% and $\frac{1}{4}$
The pupils could draw on 1cm squared paper a 5×20 rectangle, colour 50% of it and label it as shown below.

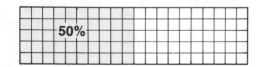

The rectangle should then be cut out and folded 'vertically' in half. Through discussion the equivalence of 50% and $\frac{1}{2}$ should be established. A similar approach could be used for 25% and $\frac{1}{4}$. Note that this method avoids the need to simplify a common fraction, such as $\frac{50}{100}$ or $\frac{25}{100}$.

2 Equivalence of 10% and $\frac{1}{10}$
This could be established using pairs of diagrams, an example of which is given here.

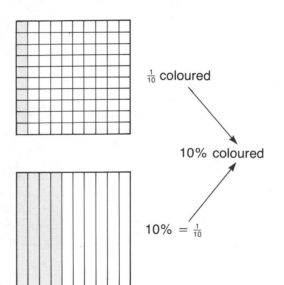

$\frac{1}{10}$ coloured

10% coloured

$10\% = \frac{1}{10}$

Detailed notes

Tinted panels The calculations described in the panels are intended to be carried out mentally and should be discussed with the pupils.

Equipment

For the Introductory activity: 1 cm squared paper, coloured pencils, scissors.

S45

Percentages:
Fractions as
percentages

N3d/
5 → 6
HD2c/
5 → 6

D/E2
I/D1
RTN/D4

Content

- Interpretation of information presented in tabular form
- Interpretation of a bar graph
- Expression of fractions with denominator 100 as percentages
- Construction of a pie chart.

Equipment

Coloured pencils.

Detailed notes

Q1 Ensure that pupils understand how to complete the table by referring to the first row.

Q2 Check that the pupils realise that one interval represents 2 pupils on the horizontal axis.

Q3 Pupils should colour the completed pie chart using different colours for each sector.

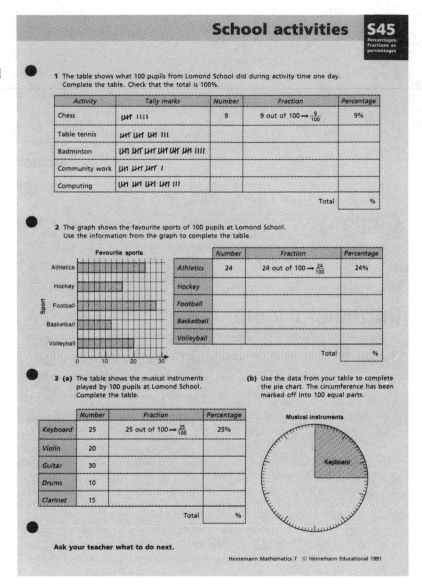

Content

- Interpretation of information presented in visual form
- Percentages in common fraction form
- Percentages of a quantity, without a calculator
- Calculation of percentage increase and decrease.

The percentages are restricted to 25%, 20% and 10%.

Detailed notes

Q1 to 3 Sufficient information has been given on the page to enable pupils to complete the work without teacher help. A problem solving approach should be used. The essential mathematical knowledge is not new although it is presented in unfamiliar situations.

Equipment

None.

E30
Percentages:
Percentage
increase and
decrease

N3c,
4b/5 → 6

PSE
I/E1
RTN/D4
FPR/E3

Content

- Interpretation of information presented in visual form
- Expression of vulgar fractions with denominators 200, 50 and 150 as percentages
- Expression of one number as a percentage of another using equivalent fractions.

Detailed notes

Q1 Each fraction requires simplification to become a fraction with denominator 100. For example:

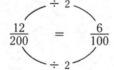

Q3 Having found the total number in each age group, pupils should check that the overall total is 150. To express each fraction with denominator 100, two steps are required. For example:

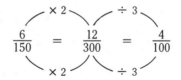

Additional activity

Car survey
Pupils should be encouraged to carry out a survey of their own.
For example, 150 or 200 people could be questioned as to the colour of their car and the number of each colour expressed as a percentage of the total. Using equivalent fractions to find percentages can give rise to difficulties and answers in some cases might be approximate. For example, 56 cars out of 300 are red

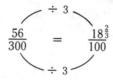

About 19% of cars are red.

Equipment

Coloured pencils.

E31
Percentages:
Fractions as
percentages

N3d/6

I/E1
RTN/E
E+

96	97
× by multiples of 10 and 100	× and ÷ by multiples of 10 and 100

CONTENT AND DEVELOPMENT

Core

Earlier in Heinemann Mathematics 7 the ability to calculate mentally was applied in the use of single-digit calculations to estimate answers to addition and subtraction of large numbers and in the use of the associative property (Part 1); and in the estimation of money totals (Part 2).

In *Other methods 3*, different methods of computation are used as alternatives to standard written techniques. Emphasis is placed on mental calculation. The section covers:

- multiplication of a two-digit number and
  - a single-digit number
  - 10 and multiples of 10
  - 100 and multiples of 100
- multiplication and division of money amounts by 100 and multiples of 100
- division of three- and four-digit numbers by
  - a single-digit number
  - 10, multiples of 10, and by 100.

National Curriculum (England and Wales)

N3bc, 4b

Mathematics 5–14 (Scotland)

MD/C2, D1, D2, E1, E2

Equipment

None.

Content

Alternative methods for multiplication of a two-digit number and
- a single-digit number
- 10 and multiples of 10
- 100 and multiples of 100.

Mental calculation is encouraged using the distributive and associative properties.

Detailed notes

Panels above Q1, Q2, Q6	The suggested methods should be discussed with the pupils who should then be encouraged to devise their own methods. For example, when multiplying using a multiple of 10 or 100 it is also possible to multiply by 10 or 100 first.
Panel above Q4	This alternative method for multiplication by 50 should be discussed.

Additional activity

Multiplication by 25

Able pupils may be challenged to find a way of multiplying a two-digit number by 25 mentally. For example, for 38×25 it is possible to multiply by 100 and then divide by 4,

$$38 \times 100 = 3800 \text{ and } 3800 \div 4 = 950$$

It is also possible to divide by 4 *first*,

$$38 \div 4 = 9.5 \text{ and } 9.5 \times 100 = 950$$

although, as in this case, any resulting decimal may cause greater difficulty.

Equipment

None.

Content

Alternative methods for
- multiplication of money amounts by 100 and multiples of 100
- division of money amounts by 100 and multiples of 100
- division of three- and four-digit numbers by a single-digit number, 10, multiples of 10, and by 100.

Mental calculation is encouraged using the associative property.

Detailed notes

Panel above Q1 and Q5	These important rules for multiplication and division by 100 of money amounts should be stressed.
Panel above Q2	Multiplication of a money amount by a multiple of 100 is better done in the reverse order from that used when numbers only were involved. Multiplying by 100 *first* has the advantage of changing the pence to pounds. However, some pupils may prefer to continue multiplying by the single-digit number first.
Panels above Q4 and Q6	The division by 10 and by 100 is done *last*. Some pupils may be able to suggest that this could be done first if preferred.

Additional activity

Division by 50

Able pupils may be challenged to find a different method of mentally dividing by 50. For example, for $950 \div 50$, it is possible to multiply by 2 and then divide by 100,

$$950 \times 2 = 1900 \text{ and } 1900 \div 100 = 19$$

It is also possible to divide by 100 *first*,

$$950 \div 100 = 9.5 \text{ and } 9.5 \times 2 = 19$$

although, as in this case, any resulting decimal may cause greater difficulty.

Equipment

None.

98	99	100 W40 W41
Rate per minute	Rate per second	Speed

CONTENT AND DEVELOPMENT

Core

In the *Time* section (on pages 101–107 of these notes), pupils were involved in revising and consolidating various aspects of time, for example, finding the date a week later or earlier than a given date, using diaries, matching 24-hour times to am and pm times, and calculating times and durations using timetables.

Rate and speed introduces the following topics:

- concepts of rate per minute and rate per second
- calculation of rate per minute and rate per second
- speed, as a special example of rate, in metres per second, kilometres per hour and miles per hour.

This work is practically based and the emphasis throughout is on real-life data.

National Curriculum (England and Wales)

N4ad
SM4c

Mathematics 5–14 (Scotland)

T/D3, D4

RELATED ACTIVITIES

Rate and speed in the environment
Many pupils will have heard the terms rate and speed without understanding the concepts. Finding references to these terms in magazines and newspapers, for example, in sports and leisure events, is likely to arouse interest in the mathematics of these pages.

It would increase interest and understanding if this aspect of mathematics could be linked to sports events within the school.

EQUIPMENT

A watch or clock which measures in seconds, calculator, metric measuring tape (10 m or 20 m length), scissors, glue.
For the Introductory activities: ream of paper, playing cards, a novel.

Content

- Observation of the frequency of an event in a fixed time
- Expressing an observation as a rate per minute
- Calculation of rates per minute.

Introductory activities

1 How long is a minute?
Ask the pupils to estimate the duration of a minute from a given starting time. They should have their eyes closed and raise a hand when they believe a minute has passed. Two pupils should act as recorders. They should list each pupil's name beside the numbers 1, 2, 3 and so on, as each hand is raised. The minute is noted as a line across the list. The completed list can allow pupils to see if they estimated shorter or longer than a minute.

2 What can we do in a minute?
Create four groups and allocate each group one of the following activities. Find for one minute.
- how often a pupil can take off and put on a jacket
- how many sheets of paper in a pile can be counted
- how many playing cards can be dealt, collected and dealt, etc.
- how many lines of a book can be read aloud.

Each group should organise for itself:
- how the timing of the minute is to be carried out
- who does this timing
- how a record of what happens is to be kept
- who keeps the record.

3 Taking a pulse
Pupils could be shown how to take a pulse, that is, to place the second and third fingers against the underside of the opposite wrist so that the beat is clearly felt. Discuss how the pulse may be counted over varying intervals, for example, 10, 20 or 30 seconds. Explain that 40 beats in 30 seconds is equivalent to 80 beats per minute or a rate of 80 beats per minute.

Detailed notes

Q1, 2, 3 Each member of the pair should time their partner.

Equipment

Clock or watch which measures in seconds. For Introductory activity 2: ream of paper, playing cards, a novel.

98
Rate and speed:
Rate per minute

N4a/5
SM4c/
5 → 7

T/D4

Content

- Measurement of distance travelled in a fixed time
- Expressing distance travelled as a rate per second
- Calculation of rates per second.

Introductory activities

1 How long is a second?
Ask the pupils if they know how to time in seconds by saying 'one elephant, two elephants, three elephants, etc' and discuss how the duration of one second is equated to each spoken phrase. Explain that one second is so short that we tend to time an activity for ten seconds and find the average rate per second by dividing by ten.

2 What can we do in a second?
Create four groups. Ask each group to find for ten seconds, using a stop-watch:
- how many times one pupil can click his or her fingers
- how many times one pupil can rise on his or her toes
- how many playing cards can be dealt
- how many words from a book can be read aloud.

Pupils should then calculate each activity as a rate per second, with answers expressed to the nearest whole number.

Detailed notes

Q1, 2 Pupils may require chalk to mark the distances.

Q4, 5 Discuss with pupils the meaning of 'speed' and when they have heard or used the term. Conclude that speed is a special name for rate where *distance travelled* is related to time.

Additional activity

Records
Encourage pupils to find reference books which give record speeds for animals, for transport and for sports events. A display could be made of the findings.

Equipment

Watch or clock which measures in seconds, metric tape (about 20 m), calculator, chalk. For Introductory activity 2: playing cards, a novel.

99
Rate and speed:
Rate per second

N4a/5
SM4c/
5 → 7

T/D3, D4

100
W40
W41
Rate and
speed:
Speed

N4a/5;
4d/5 → 6
SM4c/
6 → 7

T/D4

Content

- Calculation of speed in metres per second and kilometres per hour
- Relative speed in kilometres per hour (animals) and miles per hour (vehicles).

The formula speed = $\dfrac{\text{distance}}{\text{time}}$ is *not* introduced.

Introductory activity

Calculating a speed
Use an example such as

'The tractor covered 820 metres in 4 minutes. Find the tractor's speed in metres per second.'

to show pupils how to record the steps for the calculation and to remind them of how to interpret the answer found by using the calculator, like this:

4 minutes is 240 seconds.
In 1 second the tractor covered
$820 \div 240 = 3\cdot4166666$ metres
The tractor's speed is about 3 metres per second.

Equipment

Calculator, paste, scissors.

Which speed? W40
Rate and speed

Detailed notes

100 How fast?
Rate and speed: Speed

Eric ran 1500 metres in 4 minutes 12 seconds.
4 minutes 12 seconds is 252 seconds.

In **1 second** he ran $1500 \div 252 = $ `5.9523809` metres.
His running speed was about **6 metres per second**.

1 Find each speed in metres per second to the nearest whole number.

(a) Carl ran 200 metres in 24 seconds.
(b) Donna ran 400 metres in 65 seconds.
(c) Lisa ran 100 metres in 14 seconds.
(d) Dick cycled 500 metres in 30 seconds.
(e) Evelyn swam 100 metres in 58 seconds.
(f) Frank rowed 2000 metres in 8 minutes 25 seconds.

A Boeing 747 flew 5600 kilometres in 8 hours.
In **1 hour** it flew $5600 \div 8 \approx 700$ kilometres.
Its speed was **700 kilometres per hour**.

2 Find each speed in kilometres per hour to the nearest whole number.

(a) 5400 km in 9 hours
(b) 868 km in 7 hours
(c) 1008 km in 24 hours
(d) 402 km in 6 hours
(e) 816 km in 12 hours
(f) 384 km in 8 hours

(g) Helicopter → 495 km in 4 hours
(h) Bicycle → 125 km in 6 hours
(i) Power boat → 483 km in 8 hours
(j) Yacht → 55 km in 3 hours

3 Do Workbook pages 40 and 41.

1 Cut out the six speed labels from the edge of this page. These speeds are in **kilometres per hour**.

2 Stick on the speed label which you think matches each picture.

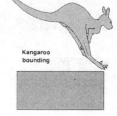

Woman walking

Golden eagle diving

Ostrich running

Tortoise crawling

Penguins swimming

Kangaroo bounding

Do Workbook page 41.

Do not cut out this section

48 kilometres per hour

25 kilometres per hour

70 kilometres per hour

120 kilometres per hour

5 kilometres per hour

0·3 kilometres per hour

Q1 Because all speeds have been expressed as 'per second', encourage pupils to compare their answers to find
- the fastest runner,
- the fastest 'mover',
- the slowest 'mover'.

Q2 Again encourage pupils to compare and order their answers.

W40, W41 Each set of labels should be matched by considering first the fastest and the slowest movers. Then compare the others to estimate the likely order. Reference books should be used to check the estimates before pupils look at the Answer Book.

101 W39	102	103
Introduction	Vertical scales	Horizontal scales

CONTENT AND DEVELOPMENT

Core

Previous work should have included the recognition of a negative number in contexts such as reading a value from a temperature scale.

In *Negative numbers*, the work is presented in a variety of contexts and covers:

- language and notation for the recording of positive and negative numbers
- use of negative numbers in a variety of contexts
- ordering negative and positive numbers
- informal calculations involving negative numbers.

National Curriculum (England and Wales)

N2b, 3c

Mathematics 5–14 (Scotland)

RTN/E1
AS/E4

RELATED ACTIVITIES

Temperatures
Pupils could undertake an investigation into temperatures. The type of information gathered could be found in encyclopedias, the *Guinness Book of Records* or from other school departments. Pupils could be asked to find

- the world's lowest and highest recorded temperature
- Britain's lowest and highest recorded temperature
- the freezing point of water
- the temperature of the body
- the freezing point of alcohol
- the temperature inside a fridge.

This information could be displayed on a large 'thermometer'.

EQUIPMENT

Red and blue coloured pencils.
For the Introductory activities: calculator, blank paper, ruler.

101
Negative
numbers:
Introduction

N2b/3

RTN/E1

Content

- Language and notation for the recording of negative and positive numbers.

Introductory activities

1 Thermometer scales
Discuss where negative numbers are used in everyday life. For example, television weather forecasts. Discussion should highlight the following

- water freezes at 0°C, zero degrees Celsius
- a Summer temperature could be 23°C, 23 degrees *above* freezing or *positive* 23° Celsius
- a Winter temperature could be ⁻3°C, 3 degrees *below* freezing or *negative* 3° Celsius.

2 Number patterns using a calculator
A recording sheet containing unmarked scales could be prepared and duplicated for pupils. Alternatively, pupils could measure out scales on blank paper.
Ask pupils to enter 4 in the calculator and label the uppermost mark 4.

4

They now press ▬ 1 to give 3 which is written on the scale.
Continue subtracting 1 and use the results to label the marks on the scale until the scale is complete. Note that different calculators may display the negative symbol in different ways. The term 'negative' and recording such as ⁻3 should be discussed. The activity can be repeated for different starting displays and using different amounts for subtraction. For example, begin with 20 and repeatedly subtract 5.

Detailed notes

Panel above Q1 Ensure pupils understand
- the freezing temperature of water
- the different methods of recording.

Equipment

For the Introductory activity: calculator, blank paper, ruler.

W39
Negative
numbers:
Introduction

N2b, 3c/
4 → 5

RTN/E1

Content

- Ordering negative and positive numbers.

Introductory activity

Extension of the number line
Draw a number line showing the first few positive whole numbers.

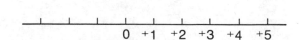

Discussion should highlight
- numbers to the left are smaller than numbers to the right. +2 is smaller than +5
- numbers to the right are greater than numbers to the left. +5 is greater than +2

Extend the number line to the left and ask pupils which numbers are indicated by the new marks. After entering these numbers emphasise that the two statements above still apply and discuss some specific cases. For example:
⁻2 is smaller than +2 and +2 is greater than ⁻2
⁻4 is smaller than 0 and 0 is greater than ⁻4
⁻6 is smaller than ⁻3 and ⁻3 is greater than ⁻6.

Detailed notes

Q1 For pupils unfamiliar with Hi-fi systems it will be necessary to discuss the technical terms mentioned on the page, namely, graphic equaliser, tone, bass and treble.
Q3 Although the expected form of recording is illustrated some pupils may require additional explanation.

Equipment

Red and blue coloured pencils.

Content

- Ordering negative and positive numbers
- Representation of negative numbers on a vertical number line
- Informal addition of integers and subtraction of a whole number from an integer.

Introductory activity

Temperature on a vertical scale
Draw a vertical number line to represent a thermometer on the blackboard. Discussion should highlight that

- it gets *hotter* as you move *up* the scale
- it gets *colder* as you move *down* the scale.

Demonstrate how to use the number line to find the temperature if, for example, it starts at $-3°C$ and rises by $7°$. This can be done by starting at -3 and counting up 7 to finish at 4.

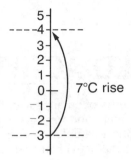

102
Negative numbers:
Vertical scales

N2b, 3c/
4 → 5

RTN/E1
AS/E4

Another example could be:
What will the thermometer show if the temperature
(a) starts at $-2°C$ and rises by 6 degrees
(b) starts at $7°C$ and falls by 9 degrees?
The number line can also be used to demonstrate how to find the rise and fall of a temperature. For example:
By how many degrees does the temperature
(a) rise when it goes from $-3°C$ to $7°C$?
(b) fall when it goes from $2°C$ to $-5°C$?

Equipment

None.

Content

- Representation of negative numbers on a horizontal number line
- Informal addition of integers and subtraction of a whole number from an integer.

Introductory activity

Temperature on a horizontal scale
Draw a horizontal number line representing a thermometer on the blackboard.

103
Negative numbers:
Horizontal scales

N2b, 3c/
4 → 5

RTN/E1
AS/E4

Discussion should highlight

- the similarity between the horizontal number line and the vertical number line
- that numbers get *bigger* as you move to the *right*
- that numbers get *smaller* as you move to the *left*.

Demonstrate how to use the number line to find the temperature if, for example, it starts at $4°C$ and falls by $9°$. This can be done by starting at 4 and counting 9 places to the left to finish at -5.

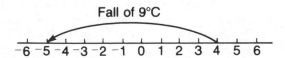

Examples similar to those in the Introductory activity for Core Textbook page 102 should be discussed and demonstrated to the class.

Equipment

None.

104 W22 W37	W38	105 W20 W26
Geometric shapes	Tessellations	Patterns

CONTENT AND DEVELOPMENT

Core

Pupils should have had previous experience of fitting together sets of plastic or gummed shapes to discover which ones formed tilings and which ones did not.

In *Tessellations*, this work is revised and extended to cover:

- construction of tilings using geometrical shapes
- construction of tilings using composite shapes.

National Curriculum (England and Wales)

UA3ce
SM2ab, 3bc

Mathematics 5–14 (Scotland)

PSE
RS/D2, D5

RELATED ACTIVITIES

Geometrical patterns often appear in floor coverings, wallpapers and furnishing materials. Ask pupils to collect samples that show tilings and describe the mathematical shapes used in each.

EQUIPMENT

Scissors, glue, coloured pencils, gummed shapes or tiles of regular pentagons, regular hexagons, regular octagons, large sheets of paper.

Content

- Naming shapes
- Construction of tilings using triangles and quadrilaterals
- Investigation of tilings with regular shapes and composite shapes.

Organisation

Pupils should work in small groups. This will allow them to pool the shapes from the Workbook to make a good sized display. They could also share some of the tasks.

Introductory activities

1 Making tiling patterns
Plastic, card or gummed paper shapes could be used to make tilings like those on Core Textbook page 104. Different pupils in the group could use different sets of shapes to lay out tilings on a desk top or create wall posters.

In making some tilings, a row of shapes may have to be 'turned round' or placed 'upside down' as shown.

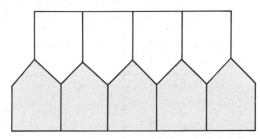

The shapes used could include common types which do form a tiling on their own, for example: equilateral triangles, isosceles triangles, right-angled triangles, squares, rectangles, rhombuses, parallelograms, kites.

2 Tiling with regular shapes
Pupils should be given the opportunity to attempt tilings using regular shapes. They should find that only three regular shapes tile, namely, the equilateral triangle, the square and the regular hexagon.

Regular pentagons and regular octagons do *not* form a tiling *on their own*.

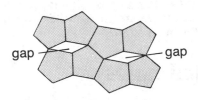

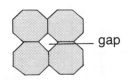

Detailed note

> **Q2b** When tiling, these shapes should not be turned over. Every second shape is *turned round* to make the tiling pattern.

Equipment

Scissors, glue, coloured pencils, gummed shapes or tiles of regular pentagons, regular hexagons, regular octagons, large sheets of paper.

104
W22
W37
Tessellations: Geometric shapes

SM2ab, 3bc/4

PSE RS/D2, D5

Content

- Tiling with composite tiles made from two or more geometrical shapes
- Working methodically to produce and record tiling patterns.

Detailed notes

> **Q1** The edges of the tilings give clues to the shape of the repeated composite tile. Each composite tile is made from two shapes: hexagon and square.

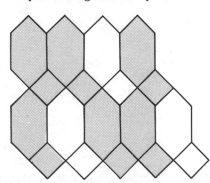

> **Q2** Different repeating tiles form the same pattern.

Equipment

Coloured pencils.

105
W20
W26
Tessellations:
Patterns

UA3ce/4
SM2b,
3bc/5

PSE
RS/D5

Content

- Tiling patterns using tiles with rotational symmetry
- Working methodically to produce and record tiling patterns.

Organisation

Small groups (4 to 8 pupils) should work together to ensure that there are enough tiles available to make worthwhile patterns.

Detailed notes

Q1 Pupils may also find this pattern.

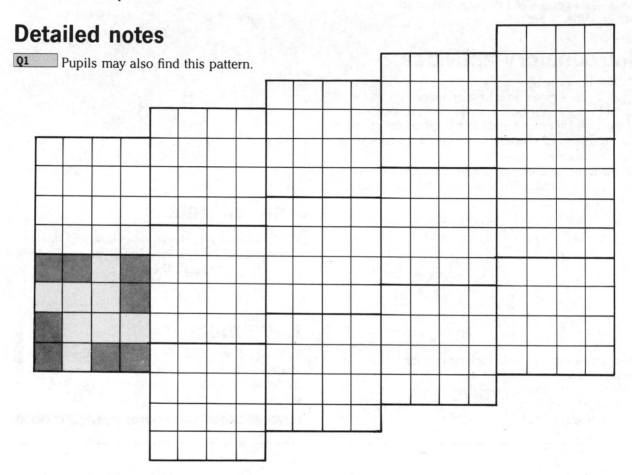

Q2 Each group should colour their tiles in a systematic way using agreed colours.

Q3a The triangular tiles produce unexpected parallelograms when they are put together in a tiling.

Equipment

Scissors, glue, coloured pencils, large sheets of paper.

CONTENT AND DEVELOPMENT

Core

Handling data 1 (on pages 26–31 of these notes) covers interpretation and construction of bar graphs, combined bar graphs and also pie charts, range and mean, collection and organisation of data. In *Handling data 2* (on pages 65–70 of these notes), new work covers interpretation and construction of line-graphs in 'trend' graph and constant-gradient 'conversion' graph forms.

Handling data 3 consolidates earlier work and also covers:

- the design and use of observation sheets in data collection
- use of class intervals in the collection, organisation and display of data
- interpretation and construction of frequency tables and frequency diagrams including choosing suitable class intervals.

Most of the data used is discrete. Some continuous data involving time and weight is included but it is rounded to the nearest whole unit and in effect is treated as discrete. A full treatment of continuous data appears in Heinemann Mathematics 8.

Graphs are also used where appropriate in other sections throughout the course.

National Curriculum (England and Wales)

UA3e
HD2acef

Mathematics 5–14 (Scotland)

C/E1, E2
O/E1
D/D2
I/D1, E1
E+

RELATED ACTIVITIES

Handling data in the environment
Pupils will use handling data techniques in other areas of the curriculum such as science and geography. They could collect examples of tables and graphs in which class intervals are used from these subject areas, for example, from textbooks or from the results of practical experiments or investigations. They could also collect examples from newspapers and magazines with a view to mounting these in a wall display.

EQUIPMENT

Calculator, 2 mm, $\frac{1}{2}$ cm and 1 cm squared paper, blank paper.

106

Handling
data 3:
Designing
observation
sheets

UA3c/4
HD2a/4

C/E1
D/E1
E+

Content

- Identification of key features in the design of observation sheets for collecting data.

Organisation

Pupils should work in groups of three or four. Each group's findings for Q1 and Q2 may be reported to the teacher or to the class before progressing further.

Pair the groups for Q2, where they compare their observation sheets, and for Q4, where each group makes the entries on the other group's observation sheet.

Detailed notes

Q1 Pupils will require time to discuss the three examples of observation sheets. They should be encouraged to keep their written comments brief. They may note that
- each heading should only be used once
- letters are better grouped together
- tally marks are easier to count than ticks or letters
- it is useful to have totals recorded.

Q2 Pupils could be led to discuss how each of them might answer the question. This is likely to help them to break up the question into categories and define 'one day'. The pupils may wish to experiment with more than one layout before making a decision. When comparing their observation sheets, pupils should justify why they consider features to be good or poor. Written comments should be brief, possibly resticted to lists of good features.

Q3a Pupils could discuss the way in which each of them attempted to write the words. For example:
- words beginning with a, then c . . . .
- two letter words, three letter words . . .
- any words in any order, and so on.

Q3b Pupils will realise that many of their words might not be recorded on the given observation sheet. This may give rise to a discussion that the question should reflect the words to be recorded or that the sheet should be altered.

Q4 Completing the given task individually will result in a range of data. The group must decide if they wish to record all or only some of their data. The ease with which they can complete their observation sheet should influence their decision about its effectiveness. Again written comment should be brief.

Additional activity

Choosing an issue
Pupils should have the opportunity to work as a group to specify an issue for which they wish to collect data. They should produce a suitable observation sheet, collect and organise the data then report on their findings.

Equipment

A supply of blank and squared paper.

Content

- Interpretation of information from a table
- Calculation of mean and range
- Organisation of data in a frequency table using suitable class intervals
- Display of this data in a frequency diagram.

For the work of these pages the appropriate class intervals are given.

Organisation

Allow pupils to complete Q1 and Q2. After discussion of their answers introduce the term 'class interval' as indicated in the Introductory activity.

Introductory activity

Class intervals
Discuss the data from the sponsored swim with the pupils. Indicate that unlike previous work relating to compilation of a frequency table, for example on Core Textbook page 25, the range of data in this case is large. In order to obtain a *broad* idea of how results are distributed, it is possible to group these results in *class intervals*. Explain what is meant by this term, referring to the panel after Q2:

- a class interval includes several values
- class intervals are of equal size, in this case 5, that is, 1 to 5, 6 to 10, 11 to 15 and so on
- the lowest value or 'number of lengths completed' (4) is in the first class interval, and the highest value or 'number of lengths completed' (29) is in the last class interval.

Ask questions such as 'In which interval should 18 be placed?'

HD2c/4; 2e/5

D/D2
I/D1
E+

Equipment

Calculator.

Detailed notes

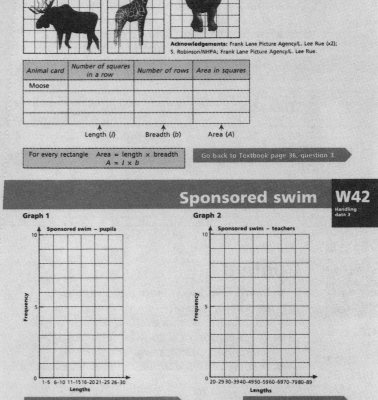

Acknowledgements: Frank Lane Picture Agency/L. Lee Rue (x2); S. Robinson/NHPA; Frank Lane Picture Agency/L. Lee Rue.

Q3c Check that the total in the frequency column is equal to the total number of swimmers.

W42, graphs Note the way class intervals are labelled on the horizontal axes.

Q4b The class interval size in this case is 10. It should be easier to complete the frequency table by working down each column of the Record sheet in turn. Check that the total in the frequency column agrees with the total number of swimmers.

137

108
W43
Handling
data 3:
Choosing class
intervals

UA3e/4
HD2c/6

C/E1, E2
D/D2
I/D1
E+

Content

- Use of different sizes of class interval for a single set of data
- Identification of class intervals where the number of intervals is given/has to be determined
- Organisation of data in a frequency table choosing suitable class intervals
- Collection and organisation of data and its display as a frequency diagram.

Organisation

Allow pupils to attempt Q1 on both pages before leading the suggested discussion. The Introductory activity should be linked with Q2 to Q4 on the Core Textbook page.

Introductory activity

Choosing class intervals
List as shown the number of correct answers by each pupil who took part in a 'Sponsored Spelling' event.

$$4 \ 12 \ 15 \ \ 9 \ 13 \ \ 7$$
$$17 \ 25 \ 21 \ 17 \ 13 \ 15$$
$$10 \ 18 \ 15 \ \ 2 \ 16 \ 20$$
$$14 \ 20 \ \ 5 \ 12 \ 23 \ 11$$
$$7 \ 14 \ 17 \ \ 9 \ 18 \ \ 5$$

Discuss a procedure for determining the size of the class intervals:
- find the highest and lowest values and then the range $(25 - 2 = 23)$
- try to have from 5 to 12 class intervals, ensuring that the lowest and highest values are in the first and last intervals respectively.

Trial size of interval	Class intervals	Number of intervals	
2	1–2, 3–4, 5–6, . . . 25–26	13	too many
5	1–5, 6–10, 11–15, 16–20, 21–25	5	suitable
4	1–4, 5–8, . . . 25–28	7	more suitable

Detailed notes

Q1, **W43,Q1** Discussion of the key ideas is essential. In each graph
- the same data is displayed
- the class interval sizes are different
- the lowest value (1) is in the first class interval and the highest value (24) is in the last class interval.

W43,Q3 It should be made clear that the first class interval need *not* have
- 1 as its lowest value
- the lowest value as its lowest value.

Q4 This question provides an opportunity for pupils to raise funds for a deserving cause.

Equipment

2 mm or $\frac{1}{2}$ cm squared paper.

109
Handling
data 3:
Choosing class
intervals

HD2cf/6

D/D2
I/D1, E1
E+

Content

- Interpretation of information from a frequency diagram
- Calculation of range
- Organisation of data in a frequency table choosing suitable class intervals
- Display of this data as a frequency diagram.

Detailed notes

Q2b,3b Pupils should be reminded to total the frequency columns of each frequency table to check that all data has been accounted for.

Q2b A suitable class interval size would be 10, that is class intervals of 40 to 49, 50 to 59 and so on.

Q3b A suitable class interval size would be 5, that is class intervals of 45 to 49, 50 to 54 and so on.

Q2c,3c Use 1 cm squared paper. Each graph should be given a title and have its axes labelled.

Equipment

1 cm squared paper.

CONTENT AND DEVELOPMENT

Core

In previous work many mathematical ideas have been presented in contexts. In Parts 1 and 2 of Heinemann Mathematics 7, extensive contextual work was based on the catalogue for the imaginary firm 'Goodies' which is supplied as part of the Core Textbook. Another extended context 'The School Concert' appears in the Extension Textbook.

This second extended context in the Core Textbook, 'The Field Study Week', simulates a study trip by a school party from the fictitious Gladeside school to a youth hostel, the Invercarron Field Centre.

The pupils are involved in various activities including

- planning the trip
- exploring the forests and hills around Invercarron, including orienteering
- visiting a local village
- mounting an open night at Gladeside school.

The mathematical content includes

- calendar work
- the four operations involving number, money and measures
- shape recognition, enlargement, symmetry and co-ordinate work
- bearings and scale drawings
- problem solving processes including
  - interpretation of information presented in written and visual form
  - selection of materials for a task
  - guess and check strategies.

General advice concerning the purpose and management of an extended context can be found on page T6 of these notes.

National Curriculum (England and Wales)

UA2acd, 3b, 4e
N2b, 3cd, 4b
A3b
SM2bcd, 3ad, 4a

Mathematics 5–14 (Scotland)

PSE
I/E1, E3
RTN/D4, E2
AS/C4, D1, D2
MD/C1, D, D3, D4, E1
FPR/E3
ME/D1, E5
T/C2, C3, C4, D1, D2, D4
PFS/E3
RS/D2, D3
PM/D2, D3, E1, E3
S/D2
A/D1, D2
E+

RELATED ACTIVITIES

School outings
Brochures and leaflets relating to school trips, youth hostels and so on can be studied in school. Comparison can then be made between a real trip and the simulated trip.

It may also be possible to undertake a real field study trip, whether for as short as a day or as long as a week, will depend on individual schools. Such a trip will give pupils the experience of many of the activities mentioned in the context and develop the cross curricular aspects of the section.

EQUIPMENT

Coloured pencils, ruler, 1 cm, 2 cm and 5 cm squared paper, large sheet of centimetre squared paper (40 cm × 40 cm approx.), card, a current calendar, cardboard protractor from W22, calculator, string, thread or pipe-cleaner, glue, scissors.
For Additional activity: long metric tape.

110
111
Extended
Context:
The field
study week

UA2c,
3b/4
N4b/5
SM2bc/4

PSE
I/E1, E3
AS/D1
MD/C1, D3
T/C4, D4
RS/D2
S/D2
E+

Content

- Interpretation of information presented in written form
- Calendar work
- The four operations involving money
- Shape recognition, symmetry and enlargement
- Problem solving involving a systematic approach to calculations.

Introductory activity

Introducing the Field Study week
Set the scene for the context by discussing with the pupils what a Field Study week is and then find out about their own experiences. For example: Have any pupils stayed in a youth hostel or gone hill walking? Have any pupils done any map reading or orienteering?

Discuss the planning needed to organise a successful Field Study week; suitable dates, number of pupils and staff to go on the trip, booking the youth hostel, cost, how to pay for the trip, meeting with parents and so on.

Discuss the letter sent out by the headteacher and ask questions relating to it, for example: 'Why do you think the letter was sent out as early as the middle of January?' 'Do you think that paying the cost of the Field Study week over a period of weeks is a good idea?'

Equipment

A current calendar, 1 cm squared paper, coloured pencils or pens, large sheet of 1 cm squared paper (40 cm × 40 cm approx.), card.

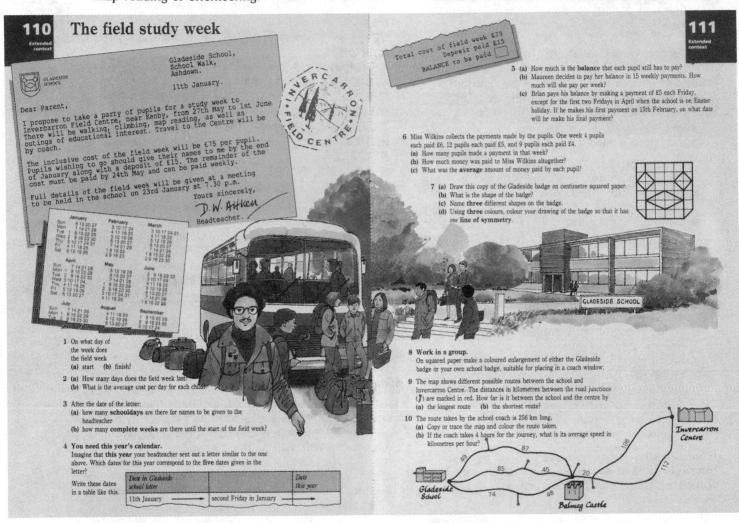

Detailed notes

Q2a The duration of the Field Study week includes both the day of departure and the day of return.

Q4 The pupils have to imagine that in the headteacher's letter for the *current* year each 'time of the year' corresponds to the 'time of the year' in the Gladeside school letter. For example, the Gladeside school Field Study week was due to start on the 27th May, which was the last Monday in May. The pupils therefore have to find the date of the last Monday in May for the current year.

Q5 Explanation of the term 'balance' may be required.

Q7d The hexagon *shape* of the school badge has one line of symmetry. The badge has to be coloured, using three colours, so that the coloured drawing retains the line of symmetry.

Q8 Each edge of the badge, drawn on 1 cm squared paper in Q7a, could be made about 6 times as long, necessitating the use of a large sheet of paper which can be stuck on card.

Q9,10 A systematic approach is needed to find all possible routes between the school and the centre and the distance of each calculated.

Content

- Interpretation of information presented in visual form
- The four operations involving length, time and area
- Expressing fractions as percentages.

Introductory activity

The view from Invercarron

Explain that the panoramic view presented across Core Textbook pages 112 and 113 is that seen from the entrance to Invercarron Centre. Discussion of the panorama should highlight

- roads are shown in red, footpaths in orange except in the spruce forest where there are three trails shown in red, yellow and blue
- distances between places indicated by the symbol 🔑 are in kilometres
- heights above sea level at certain places are given in metres; the heights of the campsite and chairlift are given as well as the hilltops
- some of the places indicated will be the subject of further study, for example the village of Kenby.

Additional activity

A daisy patch

The method of estimating the number of trees in the spruce forest can be used, for example, to find the number of daisies in a grassy area. The pupils can measure in m^2 the area of the grassy area, mark off a section of $1\ m^2$ and count the number of daisies in that section. The number of daisies in the grassy area can then be calculated by multiplying the number of daisies in the $1\ m^2$ section by the number of m^2 in the whole area.

Detailed notes

Q5 While some pupils may find the answers directly by carrying out a whole number calculation working in minutes, others may work in fractions of an hour. For example, for the yellow trail
$$5 \times 15\ min = 75\ min$$
or $5 \times \frac{1}{4}$ hour $= \frac{5}{4}$ hours $= 1\frac{1}{4}$ hours.

Q6 To find each answer, probably the simplest reasoning is 'In one quarter hour the pupils walk 1 km.
Time to walk to Black Craig is $2\frac{3}{4}$ hours ⟶ 11 quarter hours.
Distance to Black Craig is 11 km.'

Q8,9 Discuss the fact that when planning a climb, additional time has to be allowed because it will take longer to walk uphill than to walk the same distance on flat ground.

Q10 The graph represents all the ground covered by trees at the Invercarron Centre so each section of the graph represents $\frac{1}{20}$ or 5% of the ground.

Q11b There are various ways of calculating the answer. One possible method might be:
Area of spruce forest is 300 hectares (answer found in Q10).
But 1 hectare is 10 000 m^2 which is 100 times the marked out area of 100 m^2.
So 300 hectares is 300×100 or 30 000 times the marked out area.
But the marked out area contains 20 trees.
So the spruce forest will contain about 30 000 $\times$ 20 = 600 000 spruce trees.

N2b,
3cd/5
A3b/5
SM4a/7

PSE
I/E1
RTN/D4, E2
AS/D2
MD/D3, E1
FPR/E3
ME/E5
T/C2, C3, D2

Equipment

For the Additional activity: long metric tape.

114
115
Extended
Context:
The chair lift

UA2c/5
N4b/5
SM2d,
3d/5

PSE
MD/D
ME/D1
T/C3, D1,
D2
PFS/E3
PM/E1
A/D2

Content

- Interpretation of information presented in written form
- The four operations involving whole numbers, length and time
- Time – 24 hour notation, minutes and hours
- Measurement of angles to nearest 10° and expression of these as bearings
- Measurement of lengths to nearest $\frac{1}{2}$ cm and use of scale to find a true distance.

Organisation

After Introductory activity 1, the pupils could attempt Q1 to Q5. Q6 and Q7 could be attempted after Introductory activity 2.

Introductory activities

1 Chair lift
A general discussion about chair lifts, drawing upon the illustration on the page, would be useful. Questions could be posed such as 'Who has been on a chair lift?', 'Did the chair lift stop to allow you on to the chair?' and so on.

2 Direction indicators, orienteering
After a brief discussion on direction indicators, pupils should be reminded what is meant by a three-figure bearing. Discuss the use of bearings in the sport of orienteering.

Detailed notes

Q3 Some pupils may have to be reminded that the minibus needs to make two round trips to bring the whole party back.

Q4 Pupils should note that the speed is given in metres per second and the travel times are required or given in minutes.

Q5 The information must be interpreted with care. 15 pairs have to get on the empty chairs. There will therefore be 14 intervals of 10 seconds between the first and last couple.

Q6 The special 360° cardboard protractor should be used and placed on the inner circle of the viewfinder, lining up the 000° of the protractor with the N on the viewfinder as shown.

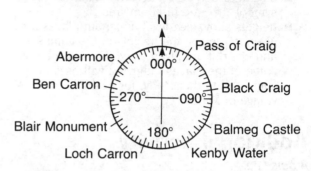

Q7 Each measured length in centimetres can be converted to the true distance in metres using a calculator if necessary.

Equipment

Ruler, cardboard protractor from W22, calculator.

W44
Extended
Context:
Orienteering

SM2d/5;
3d/5 → 6

AS/C4
MD/D4
ME/D1
PFS/E3
PM/E1
A/D1, D2

Content

- Measurement of angles to nearest 10° and expression of these as bearings
- Measurement of lengths to the nearest 0·1 cm and use of scale to find a true distance.

This work should be treated as a 'Challenge' as it requires more precise measurement and uses bearings when changing course.

Equipment

Ruler, cardboard protractor from W22, calculator.

Detailed notes

Q1 Explain to pupils that this is the same orienteering course as in Core Textbook page 115, but deals with a route from BASE, visiting each control as indicated in the table, finishing back at BASE. The distance and bearing between the pairs of controls indicated have to be found. Pupils should work systematically round the course. The distance and bearing of SQUIRREL from EAGLE would be found as shown.

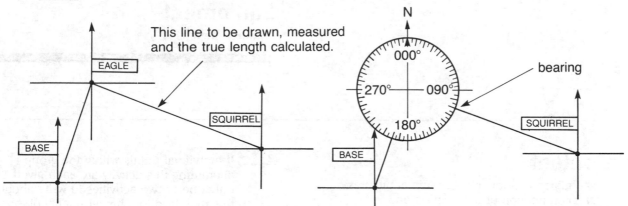

116
Extended
Context:
Kenby

SM3a/4;
2d, 3d/5

ME/D1
PFS/E3
PM/D2, D3
PM/E3

Content

- Specifying locations using co-ordinates
- Calculation of true lengths from lengths on a map using a scale
- Compass directions.

Detailed notes

Scale on map, Q4 The method used on the map to indicate the scale may be unfamiliar to some pupils. Since 4 cm represents 1 km or 1000 m, 1 cm represents 250 m.

Q6 The route should be overlaid with a piece of string, thread or pipe-cleaner bent into the shape of the route, which can then be straightened and measured in centimetres and the true distance calculated. Any measured length between 19 cm and 22 cm is acceptable, giving a true distance between 4750 m and 5500 m.

Q7,8 As North does not point to the top of the page, pupils may find it helpful to turn the page round as shown.

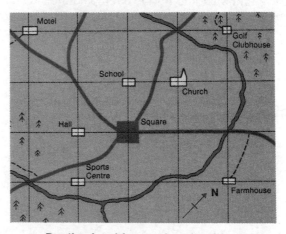

Pupils should note that the diagonals of the grid squares run either N to S or E to W while the sides of the squares run either NW to SE or NE to SW.

Equipment

Ruler, string, thread or pipe-cleaner.

117
W45
Extended
Context:
A wet evening

UA2acd/6

PSE
RS/D3

Content

■ Problem solving.

The work is investigative and should be motivating. It requires the use of a number of problem solving strategies.

Detailed notes

Square Hunt Colour a different square on each of the given diagrams on W45.

Triangle Hunt To find all the possible different triangles, several triangles need to be coloured on the same pattern as shown.

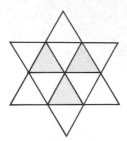

Three of the possible different triangles on the same pattern

Making Squares The rules and method of scoring are best explained by the teacher, perhaps by playing the game once or twice on a prepared blackboard grid. The pupils can play the game

■ individually, trying to score a personal 'best'

■ competitively in pairs, the winner having the higher total score or the highest individual score after several attempts by each player.

Scores can be entered on the grid as shown in the worked example. Pupils scoring forty and above should justify their route by pointing it out to the teacher or opponent.

The Glade-side Quiz Pupils should be told that each question in the Quiz, which is on Core Textbook page 118, contains a 'twist' which must be spotted in order to obtain the correct answer.

Equipment

Coloured pencils.

118
Extended
Context:
Open Night at
Gladeside

UA4e/6
SM3d/6

PSE
E+

Content

■ Enlargement of shapes (animal pictures)
■ Interpretation of information and presentation of findings in written form
■ Construction of a model
■ Problem solving.

Organisation

Q1, 2 and 3 should not be attempted individually but allocated to different groups. The results can then be displayed on the classroom wall and discussed.

Detailed notes

Q1 The pictures should be enlarged using 2 cm or 5 cm squared grids. Pupils should work in pencil until the enlargement is considered satisfactory, at which point it can be coloured.

Q2 If individual pupils within the group attempting this activity are each given only one or two activities to write about, this may lead to a higher quality of descriptive writing.

Q3 The picture of the Field Study Centre on Core Textbook page 114 may provide a basis from which to design the model. However pupils should be permitted to alter features of the building as they wish.

Q4 Pupils may already have attempted this question as part of the work on Core Textbook page 117.

Equipment

2 cm or 5 cm squared paper, coloured pencils, paints, card, glue, scissors.

CONTENT AND DEVELOPMENT

Extension

These two contexts are similar in nature to the extended context 'The Field Study Week' in the Core Textbook but are much shorter. They simulate visits by a group of pupils to a Weather Station and a Trout Farm.

The mathematical content includes

- interpretation and construction of circular bar-line and curved-line graphs
- practical measurement and experimentation
- calculation of time differences
- the four operations involving number and measure.

National Curriculum (England and Wales)

UA3bcd
N3c, 4ab
SM4c
HD2cf

Mathematics 5–14 (Scotland)

PSE
D/E, E1
I/E1
MD/E4
FPR/E1
ME/D1
PFS/E3
T/D2
E+

RELATED ACTIVITIES

A 'mini' Weather Station
The school could set up its own 'mini' weather station, keeping records of rainfall, temperature and sunshine. It might also be possible to obtain statistical records of local weather and use these to draw up tables, graphs, etc. Arrangements could be made to visit a weather station and/or a fish farm. This could be part of a cross-curricular programme involving Environmental Studies.

EQUIPMENT

Large paper circles, coloured pencil, ruler showing mm, two equal poles or canes (about 1·5 m), string, tape measure, newspaper showing times of sunrise and sunset, calculator, 1 kg dried beans, marker pen.

E34
E35
Context: Glenafton Weather Station

UA3bcd/6
N4b/5
HD2cf/6

PSE
D/E, E1
ME/D1
PFS/E3
T/D2

Content

- Interpretation and construction of circular bar-line graphs
- Use of measuring instruments to find the height of a hillock
- Use of time differences to find the direction of geographic North.

Most of this work is practical and some of it requires the use of problem solving processes.

Organisation

There are three separate activities – Q1 and Q2, Q3, Q4 and Q5, and Q6 and Q7 – which can be attempted in any order. Arrangements should be made for small groups to carry out the outdoor activities.

Detailed notes

Q1,2 Weather charts Discuss the illustrated rainfall chart beside Q1. It is a bar-line graph with each line radiating from the centre of a circle, the tinted area enclosing the radial 'spikes' indicating the annual pattern of rainfall. In Q2, the size of the circular chart to be made will depend on the scale chosen. The scale for each graph should be determined so that the highest 'value' can be represented by a line just shorter than the radius of the circle. Encourage the pupils to find their own method of producing large circles.

Q3,4,5 Measuring the height of a hillock Use a blackboard illustration like the one opposite to demonstrate the basic technique of finding the height difference between two points. The drawing at the top of E35 can then be discussed. In Q5 choose a hillock which rises steadily and whose height can be measured in about three or four steps.

Q6,7 Finding the direction of geographic North Discuss the explanation in the illustrative panel above Q6. Remind the pupils that the details apply only to the Northern Hemisphere. Point out also that the direction of North obtained by this method depends on the Sun and is therefore geographic North and not magnetic North as indicated by a compass needle.

The times of sunrise and sunset for some cities in the United Kingdom are published in several daily newspapers.

Equipment

Large paper circles, coloured pencil, ruler showing mm, two equal poles or canes (about 1·5 m), string, tape measure, newspaper showing times of sunrise and sunset.

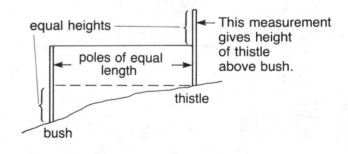

equal heights — poles of equal length — This measurement gives height of thistle above bush. — thistle — bush

E36
E37
Context: Abermore Trout Farm

N3c/5;
4a/6
SM4c/7
HD2f/5

I/E1
MD/E4
FPR/E1
E+

Content

- Interpretation of a curved-line graph
- The four operations involving number and measure
- Calculation of simple percentages of quantities
- Calculation of rate per hour/per minute/per second
- Application of a sampling method using proportion.

Detailed notes

Q1 Briefly discuss the scenario with the pupils. Ask them about the shape of the graph which can be explained as follows: 'Young trout eat little food and gain weight slowly. As they grow they eat more and gain weight faster. As they become larger they share a limited food supply, this share being sufficient to balance the energy they need.'

Q4 A possible reason for buying ten 200 g trout is that each pupil would get a whole fish. If five 400 g trout were bought each pupil would get a greater weight to eat (50 g rather than 40 g).

Panel below Q6 Discuss the panel to ensure that the pupils understand the reasoning behind the method.
3 out of 50 fish caught are marked, so 1 in every 17 fish (approximately) is marked.
Since 100 fish were marked, there should be about $100 \times 17 = 1700$ fish altogether.

Q7 Beans, peas or counters could be used to carry out this sampling activity. Ensure that when the 100 beans, taken from 1 kg of beans, are replaced, they are mixed thoroughly with the others.

Equipment

Calculator, 1 kg of dried beans, marker pen.

DETOURS IN PART 4

General advice about using the Detours can be found on page T6 of these notes.

95
Detour:
Inverse
operations

N4c/5

PSE
MD/C4, D4

Content

- Multiplication and division as inverse operations
- The use of one operation as a check for the other.

Organisation

Pupils could work in pairs to discuss the questions, using the calculator for alternate examples, rather than writing answers.

Introductory activity

Find a trio

Give a pack of, say, twenty-one cards to a group of four pupils. Seven of the cards should each have a multiplication, while the others should have the related divisions, for example:

$6 \times 8 = 48$	$48 \div 8 = 6$	$48 \div 6 = 8$

Discuss with the pupils what can be considered as a *trio* of related cards. The aim is to collect three related cards. Pupils should be dealt three

cards each. The remainder are placed in a face down pile with the top card alongside face up. Each pupil, in turn, may take the top unseen card or the top face up card. Each time a card is taken, one from the pupil's hand must be placed on the face up pile. The winner is the first player to declare a set of three related cards.

Detailed notes

Q3,4 It may need to be emphasised that only the multiplication symbol is to be used.

Q4 A trial and improvement strategy should be used.

Q4d Pupils finding $14 \times 12 = 168$ may realise without further multiplication that 13 buses are needed.

Equipment

Calculator.
For the Introductory activity: a pack of prepared cards.

S46
Detour:
Matching
shapes

SM2ab/2

RS/D2, D3

Content

- Recognition and naming of 2D shapes with 3, 4, 5 and 6 sides.

Organisation

The pupils should play the game in pairs.

Detailed notes

Line 5 The rules for this version of 'Pelmanism' are:

- shuffle the cards and place them *face down* on the table
- a player turns over two cards
- if the cards match, the player keeps the cards and has another turn
- if the cards do not match, they are turned face down again, and the turn passes to the other player
- the player with most cards at the end is the winner.

These cards should not be considered as matching.

Additional activity

Snap

Sets of cards from two Workbooks can be combined and used to play 'Snap'. A valid snap can occur by correctly matching

- a picture card with a name card
- a picture card with a picture card
- a name card with a name card.

Equipment

Card, scissors, glue.

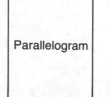

Parallelogram

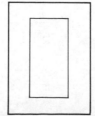

E38

Detour:
Digit sum
investigation

UA2bc,
4b/6
N3a/4

PSE

Content

An investigation of the sum of the individual digits
in two- and three-digit numbers.

- Use of problem solving strategies –
  elimination, systematic listing
- Recording findings and presenting them in
  written form
- Making and testing predictions.

Detailed notes

Q1b The appropriate ages can be listed and
then checked methodically to eliminate
all but one.

Q4,5 Encourage the use of systematic listing.
For example, for a digit sum of 5:
50, 41, 32, 23, 14 or
50, 41, 14, 32, 23.

Q7 A hint is provided on great-grandma's
birthday cake.

Q8 It is hoped that pupils record
methodically. They might also organise
their results in a table.

Additional activity

Predicting from results
Pupils could be asked to extend their table of
results for Q6 by predicting the number of
different two-digit numbers for digit sums of 7, 8
and 9. These predictions can be tested using
systematic listing.

Equipment
None.